The OKINAWA in ME:

Finally Finding
MY IKIGAI
(Reason for Being!)

Martha R. A. Fields

Editor: Kathleen Victory Hannisian, Blue Pencil Consulting
Front and back cover design: Lulu; Cindy Murphy, Bluemoon Graphics

ISBN: 978-0-9746-8020-0 (sc)
978-0-9746-8021-7 (hc)
978-0-9746-8022-4 (e)

OKI ME
Helping People World-Wide Find LIFE & WORK Success!

75 State Street, Suite 100, Boston, Massachusetts, 02109 USA

Disclaimer: This book is based upon the knowledge, ideas and opinions of Martha R.A. Fields. It has been sold to you with the understanding that she wishes to impart trends, best practices and long-lived traditions on the topics within. She is in no way providing or rendering any type of health, medical, scientific, legal, and psychological or any other professional or personal services via this book.

As is always the case, readers should consult and seek their own advice and counsel thorough health, medical, or other licensed, degreed, or certified professionals or other mechanisms deemed appropriate before drawing inferences or adapting or adopting what is described in this book. Both the publisher, author and any other parties with investments in this book totally disclaim all and every responsibility for any loss, risk, or liability, personal or otherwise, incurred as a direct or indirect consequence of applying or utilizing any contents within this publication.

Because of the dynamic nature of the Internet, any web addresses or links contained in this book may have changed since publication and may no longer be valid. The views expressed in this work are solely those of the author and do not necessarily reflect the views of the publisher, and the publisher hereby disclaims any responsibility for them.

Lulu Publishing Services rev. date: 10/04/2021

DEDICATION

To my Mervin-Norwood family and lifelong US friends in Boston, Cambridge, Cape Cod, Newton and Melrose, Massachusetts. A billion thanks to my editor Kate Victory Hannisian (Blue Pencil Consulting), Lulu Publishing, and OKI ME, LLC (Publisher). I SO appreciate all of you and my worldwide friends on the "Yeah…I Lived in Okinawa" Facebook group and those in Okinawa, Jamaica, and around the globe.

Internationally renowned photographers' and historical curators' contributions

Throughout this book, you will be treated to amazing and awe-inspiring vintage and contemporary photographs. They were contributed by professional photographers and dedicated Okinawan historical curators and photographers. These pictures helped me to vividly convey the grandeur and beauty of my precious island. I will be forever indebted to the two renowned Okinawan historical curators and photographers, Donn Cuson (www.rememberingokinawa.com) and Rob Oechsle, aka Okinawa Soba (www.flickr.com/photos/okinawa-soba/albums). I am honored that they granted me permission to use pieces from their priceless collections. I salute the painstaking work these gentlemen have done to preserve the rich history of Okinawa.

Photo courtesy: Donn Cuson
Donn Cuson & wife's wedding picture

**Photo: Rob Oechsle,
aka Okinawa Soba**

JACK RUMMEL, FRONT COVER PHOTOGRAPHER
Visit him at: https://www.Jackrummel.com.

CONTENTS

INTRODUCTION

Okinawa:
The "Land of the Immortals"

There is a Shangri-La, nirvana, utopia, and heaven on earth. It is called Okinawa!

What if I told you that a place exists in our universe that worldwide **M**edical, **R**esearch, and **S**cientific experts (I call this group by the acronym **MRS**) agree is a Shangri-La, nirvana, utopia? These uplifting words are used to describe this location by an eclectic spectrum of people ranging from millennials to mature elders. This destination holds the title of producing the healthiest and the most "supercentenarians" (individuals who live to 110 years old and beyond) per square foot than anywhere in the world.

Inhabitants have low incidences of heart disease, strokes, diabetes, and breast, prostate, and colon cancer. While individuals in this magical place do grow old, they do not tend to experience the maladies that typically accompany old age in places like the United States, including Alzheimer's, osteoporosis, dementia, and depression. Think about it:

Women at this location have the highest life expectancy on earth. They are healthy and happy. Research indicates that the elders of this society have greater natural sex hormone levels than their American counterparts and are highly active in the bedroom for most of their lives. Does this sound too unreal to be real? Believe it or not, *such a place does exist. It is called*

Okinawa, Japan. Okinawa's long reputation as the world titleholder for producing the "Longest-Lived and Healthiest People" in the world is well deserved.

What if you could live to 110+ years, be healthy, AND not get:

Photo by: Rob Oechsle "Okinawa Soba"

HEART DISEASE   **BREAST CANCER**   **COLON CANCER**   **ALZHEIMER'S**
DEPRESSION   **PROSTATE CANCER**   **DEMENTIA**   **OSTEOPOROSIS**

Does this sound too unreal to be real?

Believe it or not, such a place does exist. It is called Okinawa, Japan.
Okinawa's long reputation as the world title holder for producing the
"Longest Living and Healthiest People" on the planet is well deserved.
Not only have I done extensive research about this place,
but I was fortunate to live and grow up there.

Not only have I done extensive research about this place, but I was fortunate to live and grow up there. As an adult, I have traveled back to my beloved Okinawa and am thrilled to spread the news about this incredibly special place and share in this book how YOU can adapt their healthy longevity lessons to YOUR life even in perilous times.

Back in 2016, I had received a very generous birthday gift from a loved one. It was a trip to a destination that had been the number one item on my bucket list (things I *must* do before I die). The dream vacation was to return to Kadena Air Base in Chatan, Okinawa, a place I left at age eleven. Living in Okinawa had such a positive impact on my life that I had to see it again.

Fifty-two years after departing from Okinawa, my wish was granted and from December 2016 to January 2017, I returned to my island in the sun. On December 28, 2016, after vacationing in Okinawa for only a short time, I had rediscovered my roots and decided that I must write a book about it. I felt a duty to spread the word about why Okinawans for generations have lived to ripe old ages *and* remain healthy as they grow older.

In February 2018, I was genuinely excited about returning to Okinawa on my second trip back. I wrote part of this introduction aboard an ultra-modern American Airlines airplane equipped with state-of-the-art electronic devices that would keep me more than occupied for my long multiple-day journey. I was on a mission to accomplish two things.

First, I planned to celebrate my birthday. My second objective was to share the final manuscript of this book with some friends and colleagues in Okinawa. It was super-important to receive their feedback and blessings prior to releasing the book.

On the plane, I was focused on what lay ahead for me on the sunny East China Sea island of Okinawa. My thoughts shifted to a song that my daughter Shawna Imani Fields and her dear friend Rebecca Montgomery introduced to me when they were teenagers attending the Concord-Carlisle High School in historic Concord, Massachusetts, in 2008.

The tune is from the musical *Rent and* is titled "Seasons of Love." The lyrics move my soul. They say that there are 525,600 minutes in a year and ask, "how do you measure a year in a life?"

The song's punch line suggests that you "measure your life in love." In this book, I reveal the love that is embedded in my heart for Okinawa. It is my fervent hope that you will gain insights on how to best measure *and* achieve success within the 525,600 minutes in your life this year!

Frequently, I thank God for letting me grow up on the shores of Okinawa. I feel *so* blessed that by returning there, I finally found my Ikigai (reason for being!/why I wake up!)

Here is to your "healthy longevity" and finally finding your IKIGAI as well. It is my deepest desire that you will learn concepts in the pages ahead to achieve a life that is healthy, happy, prosperous, and wise!

En route to Okinawa, Japan somewhere between Boston, Massachusetts and Los Angeles, California USA

With all my love,
Martha R. A. Fields
Thursday, February 22, 2018, 12:38 p.m.

Postscript
02-28-2016 to 06-23-2021

Writing this book has been both exhausting and exhilarating. I began my journey to write it on December 28, 2016. The inspiration to inform readers about the people who live the longest and are the healthiest in the world occurred on "my dream of a lifetime" trip to Okinawa, Japan, where I spent part of my childhood. I fully anticipated that after writing eight books, that this one would be easy and probably take me about a year to complete it. Wow was I wrong!

It would take me five years, five months and twenty five days to finally finish it on Wednesday, June 23, 2021. When I wrote the passage above on February 22, 2018, I anticipated that the book would be completed and published within months. As life would have it, that goal would not be met. My new release date was finally established for 02-20-2020. In early February, I sent my manuscript to my publisher for what I thought would be a final round of edits before the interior book design and layout phase.

I did not, however, factor in one humongous dynamic—the COVID-19 epidemic was about to spread a worldwide pandemic. When my 02-20-2020 release date was not kept by a publisher because my editorial team got sick, it was hard for me to comprehend that life as I once knew it would change in incomprehensible ways. In the weeks ahead, I had to reach the realization that it would take longer to see the arrival of my newborn baby book.

I was *really* upset when I realized that my book would not be released on my original target date. It took a minute for me to adjust my angry attitude before I realized that slowing down my book release was a hidden blessing. I believe there are no coincidences. Perhaps the delays were to allow time to include information on how applicable this book is in a COVID-19 recovery era. The information contained in the pages ahead is more relevant than ever. Reading it will help you stay focused on what you must do to live a long and healthy life despite unpredictable times.

I am desperately trying to remain positive during these unsettling times. Each day, I strive to see the bright lining in a dark cloud and feel blessed that I am healthy. I am amazed at how radically different this planet has become in the five years since I started this book on December 28, 2016. That date was just weeks before Donald J. Trump was inaugurated as the president of the United States. He was commander-in-chief of the USA's deadliest pandemic war since the Spanish Flu in 1918 before Joe Biden was elected as the new president.

As you learn more about lessons from people who live the longest and are the healthiest, you will discover that many of them experienced COVID-19-like – or worse -- bad times in their lifetimes. Some, like the Okinawans, have witnessed unprecedented hardships that could compete with COVID-19 in the "Ain't It Awful What Happened Contest." Despite the horrendous circumstances the Okinawans faced in World War II, their "stress-resistant" personalities allowed them to emerge from their crisis better and stronger.

New discoveries are constantly evolving relative to the subjects covered ahead. I highly encourage you to use the information from this book as a starting point. For example, on December 26, 2019, the *New England Journal of Medicine* published an article on intermittent fasting that was just in time for the 2020 New Year, and a season where many had losing weight as a New Year's resolution. It provided these words of wisdom to those who might be thinking of fasting as a weight loss tool:

> "Preclinical studies and clinical trials have shown that intermittent fasting has broad-spectrum benefits for many health conditions, such as obesity, diabetes mellitus, cardiovascular disease, cancers, and neurologic disorders. Animal models show that intermittent fasting improves health throughout the life span, whereas clinical studies have mainly involved relatively short-term interventions, over a period of months. It remains to be determined whether people can maintain intermittent fasting for years and potentially accrue the benefits seen in animal models."[1]

---

[1]   Rafael de Cabo and Mark P. Mattson, "Effects of Intermittent Fasting on Aging and Disease." *New England Journal of Medicine.* 381 (December 26, 2019):2 541-2551, doi:10.1056/NEJM 1905136.

As we grapple with picking up our lives post-COVID-19 pandemic, it will be important for us to stay focused on how to practice some of the long and healthy life strategies outlined in this book.

I had the pleasure of co-writing a book, *Roadmap to Success,* with the late world-renowned author Steven Covey. His name may sound familiar because he wrote one of the most widely-read books on earth, the classic *The Seven Habits of Highly Effective People.* In it, he advised people to:

"Begin With the End in Mind."

I am using Stephen Covey's iconic words to convey the following message. By the time you complete reading through this book, my hope is you will discover at least one piece of wisdom about healthy aging that you can successfully apply to *your* life!

My journey down the road to success has mostly been a good one. I must admit, however, that life's detours have at times been excruciatingly challenging. I will discuss some of them in the following pages. Undoubtedly some of my family, friends, and colleagues will be surprised, if not stunned by what I reveal.

I will speak candidly about some deep dark pits I had to climb out of prior to and during my book journey. With hard work, grit, and determination, as well as unconditional support, love and encouragement from devoted family and lifelong friends, I arrived at my destination.

I am now a woman on a mission to spread the word about how everyone can successfully cope when faced with adversity and live long and productive lives like my dear Okinawan people. You will learn how Okinawans lived through humongous challenges and overcame them to wear the crown of the people who live the longest and are the healthiest in the world. Today, I am at a place where I moved from tragedy to triumph and out of gloom and into glee. I am the *best* that I have ever been in my *entire life.*

My journey, however, was well worth the ups and downs traveled to bring this book to fruition. You will learn more about what experts have to say about how failure is sometimes a prerequisite for success and healthy longevity. I like to say:

"Often, you learn as much, if not more, from
the downs as you do the ups in life!"

Soon, you will discover evidence-based facts and information from experts
about how your responses to stress and bad times have a huge impact on
healthy aging. If you think that life on the nirvana-like island of Okinawa
is *all* wonderful, think again. Even Shangri-La has its Gardens of Eden
filled with turbulent trials and tribulations. You will learn about how some
Okinawans' approach to tackling hard times helps them to live longer and
healthier lives.

How to approach reading this book

*Please note that this book has been written so you can read it in
sequential order, but feel free to jump around in it as you feel inspired
to do.*

The book is composed of six parts. I conducted extensive research and share
what some of the world's top Medical, Research and Science experts (I refer
to this with the acronym MRS) have found about how and why certain
populations stay healthy as they grow older.

*"To help you better digest these complex facts, I've broken
them down into to more simple and understandable
information. Said in another way, I'VE MADE THE
COMPLICATED UNCOMPLICATED!"*

Make it a priority to continue your search and journey
for wisdom on the latest healthy aging trends.

Check with your physician and healthcare
providers for specific advice

I *must* stress that you may find differing points of view from those expressed
in this book, and please remember that knowledge about healthy longevity
changes as new discoveries occur. Please *do not* use information in this
book as a replacement for receiving personal medical treatment, advice, or

diagnosis. *Always* consult with your physicians and healthcare providers about your healthcare needs.

I must be transparent with you

I want to be transparent and acknowledge something up front. While I have provided evidence-based facts and research from experts about what one must do to grow old and stay healthy, when it comes to my life, I am human and unfortunately do not always adhere to *all* the healthy longevity principles.

For example, I know that a plant-based diet is optimal, but in all honesty, I *do* like to eat meat. To better tame the carnivore in me, however, I have been experimenting with ways to integrate more leafy green vegetables (rather than cheeseburgers) into my diet. I have been exploring more yummy green smoothies and vegetable-heavy recipes. I am attempting to be more creative and am trying hard to incorporate into my own life many of the tenets followed by Okinawans and others who live long and healthy lives.

Practicing what I have learned has brought me amazing results. I am feeling the best I have ever felt. So, do not be hard on yourself if you cannot implement everything you have learned from this book immediately. Attaining healthy longevity is a lifelong journey.

I am still a work in progress, however, and I am committed to correcting my inadequacies. I like to say that:

> **"I am a perfectly imperfect person who is striving to be perfectly perfect!"**

You may be wondering, "Is it too late to start my adventure?" Absolutely not. As was mentioned earlier, the ancient philosopher Lao-tzu stated so eloquently:

> **"The journey of a thousand miles begins with one step."**

You are taking your first step towards achieving a long and healthy life by reading this book! Now that you know how the book is structured, feel free to read it in sequential order, or simply dive into any part that looks interesting to you.

Let us begin the first step of your journey.

PART I:

The "Blue Zones" and Okinawa: Where More Healthy People Live to 110+ Years than Anywhere on Earth!

Photo courtesy of: Rob Oechsle

CHAPTER 1:

Why I Wrote a Book About Okinawa and Healthy Longevity

As you learned in the Introduction, my love for Okinawa began in 1961 when I first planted my feet squarely on Okinawan soil to live on Kadena Air Base in Chatan, Okinawa. I left the island at age 11 but could never get the experience of living there out of my soul. After leaving Okinawa, I went on to do many things. I graduated from Boston University (the place where my fellow alum, Martin Luther King, Jr. received his doctorate). After graduation, a career in healthcare dominated my life for decades. During that period, I served in several executive and managerial roles at Harvard Medical School-affiliated teaching hospitals in Boston. At age 33, I became a vice president at one of them.

By the time I was 40, I was ready for more responsibility. After surveying my possible career options, I decided that it was time to become my own boss. I recognized that the reality was that as a woman and a person of color there had never been someone of my ilk to become a president of a Harvard-affiliated teaching hospital. It just was not happening at that point in history. I knew that to move up, I had to move out. I decided to become an entrepreneur and take control of my career destiny. I left my prestigious job and became President and CEO of my first company, Fields Associates, Inc., located right in the heart of Harvard Square in Cambridge, Massachusetts.

My firm would provide services around the world to Fortune 500 companies, Ivy League schools, and a variety of nongovernmental organizations. I would eventually leave my beloved home in Boston to take a hiatus and relocated to the Caribbean to pursue the feasibility of establishing an international global leadership center in Negril, Jamaica. After deciding that the time was not right for that venture, I spent several months in North Carolina's financial hub, Charlotte, and a year in the Research Triangle before deciding that the lure of Boston was too great.

Like the iconic character Dorothy from the *Wizard of Oz,* I returned in 2015 to my hometown of Boston. Just as she declared upon her return to Kansas, I realized that there was "no place like home." I left my Oz-like adventure feeling wiser for the incredible journey of living in Jamaica and North Carolina that I had taken from 2013 to 2015. I was beyond ecstatic to return to life in Boston with newfound knowledge about the world and myself.

Currently, I am CEO and President of my second company, OKI ME, LLC. It is an international management consulting company located at 75 State Street in the heart of historic Boston near Boston Harbor. My personal road to success has been tainted with a myriad of incredible downs. Despite what I have accomplished or failed at in life, from the day I left Okinawa, "The Keystone of the Pacific," in the summer of 1964, I longed to return. I vowed that someday I *would* visit that magical place which had captured and captivated my soul and spirit so many moons ago.

Achieving the number one item on my "bucket list"

As mentioned, the power of living in Okinawa was such that the number one item on my bucket list (those things you *must* do before you die,) was to revisit my cherished childhood home at Kadena Air Base. It took me 52 years to achieve that goal. I will never forget the moment I entered the base with Airman Briana Cotton, my wonderful sponsor (the person responsible for me while I was on this secured US Air Base). After *finally* returning to my beloved adopted homeland in December 2016, I learned to my surprise that I had grown up in the place in the world where people live the longest and are the healthiest! I discovered that I had been taught many of their healthy aging strategies.

My 2016 return to Kadena Air Base. Me, my US Air Force
Sponsor (Escort) Airman Briana Cotton and her dog

After being in Okinawa for only a few days and rediscovering my roots, I was certain about something. I knew that I *must* write this book. On December 28, 2016, when I was in Chatan staying at the Sunset Terrace Hotel, I began writing. In early January, while riding in a car in Okinawa with a new friend, Vicki Wilson, whom I had met on that trip, the title of my book was born. Thanks, Vicki, so much for your input.

What about the title of this book?

I chose the first part of the title of this book, *The Okinawa in Me,* because even though I had been away from Okinawa for 52 years before I returned in 2016, I always felt that what I had experienced living there stayed embedded in me. It was the place where I first learned how to love learning. Okinawan and American sensei (teachers) as well as my parents did an extraordinary job educating me by making learning not only interesting, but tons of fun.

The culture I lived in also supported educating young people and letting them wander around and explore their environment. Later, you will learn not just from me, but others who also grew up in Okinawa, that their experiences mirrored mine.

The Okinawa is in me and in you

I often tell people that "Okinawa can be in you as well." Simply stated, you, too can practice what they do and achieve a long and healthy life. In short, the Okinawa is *in (inside) of you* as well. I am often asked, "Do I have to actually go to Okinawa for it to be 'in me'?" My answer is emphatically, "No!" "The "Okinawan Spirit," which leads to a healthy and long life, can be *"in" anyone* who resides on earth. Keep reading and you will learn how to get the Okinawan Spirit and not have to visit or live there to find it.

Finally finding my IKIGAI (reason for being/waking up!)

The second part of my book's title is: *Finally Finding My Ikigai (Reason for Being!)*

WHAT IS IKIGAI?
(REASON FOR BEING!/Reason for WAKING UP)

Photo by: Rob Oechsle
Girl under a mushroom rock

A key element to achieving healthy longevity is to find what the Okinawans call:

IKIGAI
(pronounced EE-key-guy)

IKIGAI translates to "Reason for Being/Waking Up!"

It is a term derived from two Japanese words:

"iki" meaning "life or alive," and

"gai" which is a derivative of "kai" meaning "worth, value, effect or benefit."

The translation of the Okinawan word IKIGAI is the reason you wake up in the morning, your purpose (reason for being) on this earth. After finding it, you will be thrilled to arise and start your day with the knowledge that you will be adding value to people around the globe.

For generations, Okinawans have produced people who have discovered their purpose in life by finding their *IKIGAI*.

IKIGAI is about giving back to the world

Ikigai is not a selfish or negative thing. It is about feeling fulfilled in your life because you have given something back selflessly to others. It is uniquely personal. The Okinawans believe that *everyone* has an Ikigai.

For some, their Ikigai is something complex like finding the cure for cancer or Alzheimer's. For others, it is about being a teacher or boss at work and every day waking up to teach and impart wisdom to others. There are also people who believe their Ikigai is about taking fantastic care of their children or grandchildren so they can contribute in a positive way to society when they grow up.

Only *you* know what Ikigai is best for your life. As the old proverb states: "Not your mama. Not your daddy. Not your sister. Not your brother. But YOU, YOU, YOU, YOU, YOU!"

What researchers have discovered about finding your Ikigai?

Research indicates that amazing things happen for those who finally find their Ikigai. Later in this book, you will learn that experts proclaim that people who find and commit to live each day by fulfilling their Ikigai not only live longer but are healthier.

The benefits of finding one's Ikigai have also been researched. Renowned "Blue Zones" researcher and *New York Times* bestselling author Dan Buettner, and others, have even quantified the effect of one finding, then living their Ikigai. Buettner states:

> **"Research has shown that knowing your sense of purpose is worth up to seven years of extra life expectancy."[2]**

Said simply, once you find your IKIGAI the world will open to you in wondrous ways! Why? Because you will know specifically what you were put on earth to accomplish.

Okinawans for generations have produced people who have discovered their purpose in life and found their Ikigai. As you will learn, some individuals find their Ikigai by answering four powerful life-changing questions.

Would you like to discover your Ikigai and learn the four powerful and life-changing questions to find it?

---

2   Dan Buettner, *Blue Zones Solutions: Ealing and Living Like the World's Healthiest People.* (Washington, DC: National Geographic Society, 2015), 20.

If you answered yes, continue reading as you will learn about them in Part II: What Can I Do to Live a Long and Healthy Life?

Ahead, you will discover what people who grow old and stay healthy do to uncover their answers to these questions *and* achieve life and work success.

When I finally found my IKIGAI

Once I returned to Okinawa's magnificent East China Sea shores in 2016 after being away for 52 years, I knew exactly why my longing to return and bask in the magic of the island persisted throughout my life. It was during that trip, that I found my Ikigai (reason for being). While it had been staring me in the face my entire life, I had not clearly articulated what it was until I returned to my childhood home. Through that powerful experience, I discovered purpose and why I was put on this earth.

Since I found my IKIGAI in Okinawa, I thought it fitting to include the fact that I finally found my IKIGAI (reason for being!) in the book's title.

Can we talk?
Let us discuss cultural appropriation.

Photos of me taken at Ryukyu Mura Yomitan, Okinawa
February 27, 2018

Before we continue our journey, I would like to take a pit stop and speak to you upfront about the issue of "cultural appropriation." I feel that it is important that you understand my stance on this sometimes controversial issue. While only one person has personally accused me of committing cultural appropriation while I was writing this book, it is important for me to relay my position on writing about this topic as a non-Okinawan-born person. (FYI, I did have my DNA tested and found that there are East Asians in my ancestral gene pool.)

Explanation of cultural appropriation

If you are not familiar with the term "cultural appropriation," I will explain. Cultural appropriation is often seen as a derogatory term. It refers to the act of someone from a dominant culture utilizing something from another minority group of which they are not a member. This can include but is not limited to items that are related to religion, customs, social interactions, language, fashion, music, or dance.

Cultural appropriation is frowned upon because often it involves the perpetrator using whatever has been appropriated in a manner that is distasteful to a group and/or mocks that culture. Moreover, people who culturally appropriate may benefit in some way that the minority group does not (through literal profit/monetary gain, social cachet or simply lack of punishment for something deemed offensive).

Controversial cultural appropriation issues have dominated the media in recent years. One example of cultural appropriation is when the name "Redskins" or pictures of Native Americans wearing traditional outfits or looking "savage or angry" are used by non-Indian schools as mascots or the name of football teams.

Some things that are culturally appropriated are viewed as negative stereotypes or an attempt to satirize or make a caricature of that group. For example, some Native Americans in the United States do not want to be portrayed as hostile or always war-like. These individuals are offended when people from outside their groups continue to stereotype and use their cultures in that manner.

While I was writing this book, the famous Washington Redskins football team, after decades of negative backlash from native American groups, changed their name.

Often, individuals from the minority culture are offended by individuals who participate in this activity, especially when they continue to do so after complaints. Some also become angry if something from their culture was appropriated and the individual received monetary gain or notoriety from their appropriation.

I raise this topic because some reading what I have to say about Okinawa, a place where I was not born, may view me dressing in traditional Okinawan outfits, or writing about the Okinawan culture, as cultural appropriation.

Nothing could be further from the truth. My feelings about Okinawa are extremely strong and have been rooted in me for close to sixty years since I first lived on the island in 1961. As previously stated, my returning there after a long hiatus brought me new meaning about the culture. I am not trying to capitalize on this culture and people that I love dearly. I am also not attempting to silence or prevent others from talking who feel differently from me.

I totally respect and honor the people, institutions, and beliefs of the Okinawan people and do not apologize that I lived there as a child. I am grateful, humbled, and honored to have lived there and consider it my adopted homeland. It is my pure desire to extol the virtues of this amazing place so that others can learn about the incredible story of Okinawa, its people, and why it has consistently been named the home of the healthiest and longest-living people in the world. I do not want to capitalize on or culturally misappropriate anything about Okinawa. My hope is that the knowledge and wisdom you gain from this book will be incorporated into your universe.

In summary, I must point out that this is "my" story and experience about living in Okinawa and conducting research on it and the "Blue Zones" for five years. I can speak to what I have learned but encourage you check out other sources, including those with opposing views. Here are some reasons why I wrote this book and wanted to share my research about healthy longevity as well as my personal story about living in Okinawa.

Reasons I wrote this book

There were several reasons I wrote this book. I felt compelled to reveal why Okinawans for centuries have enjoyed healthy, happy, and fulfilled lives. This book also explores the expert scientific and medical research about healthy aging. Much research has been conducted to substantiate the claim that the Okinawan people are the world's longest lived and healthiest people on the globe. I wanted to present credible and evidence-based medical and scientific research on this topic.

Definitions: Centenarians and supercentenarians

To better understand the language to describe people who reach the age of 100 or older, here are some important definitions. If you are fortunate in the long-life lottery, and make it to 100 years old, you are called a "centenarian." Supercentenarians, an even rarer breed, are individuals who live to be 110 years and older.

John Robbins, author, and leading world expert on the dietary link between environment and health, explains why Okinawa is in an elite class when it comes to their population of people who achieve the 100- to 110-years-plus age milestone:

> "Scientists consider centenarians particularly important to study because they are usually living examples of successful aging. Many studies, including the New England Centenarian Study as well as the Okinawan Centenarian Study, have found that people who make it to 100 and beyond have often been remarkably healthy for most of their lives. In medical terms, they typically experience a rapid terminal decline extremely late in life, resulting in a compression of morbidity to their final years. This means that any health problems they might experience tend to take place at the very end of their exceptionally long and otherwise extremely healthy lives. *Studies of centenarians*

have found that 95 percent of those who make it to 100 have been free of major diseases into their nineties."[3]

Anecdotal data abound about how Okinawans have lived long healthy lives for many centuries. They are among the world's most studied people relative to aging. Numerous global scientists and researchers have investigated and verified Okinawa's longevity record with both quantitative and qualitative data.

Experts throughout the ages have collected and examined data about the health of this society as well as complicated medical files and surveys focused on age, nutrition, sexual habits, chronic diseases, and ability to independently complete activities of daily living (ADL). These include dressing and undressing, eating, meal preparation and feeding, safe bathroom use and maintaining continence, drinking, and bathing/grooming oneself.

More healthy 110+-year-olds per square foot in Okinawa than anywhere in the world!

"For every 100,000 inhabitants, Okinawa has 68 centenarians -- more than three times the numbers found in US populations of the same size. Even by [the] standards of Japan, Okinawans are remarkable, with a 40% greater chance of living to 100 than other Japanese people. Little wonder scientists have spent decades trying to uncover the secrets of Okinawans' longevity- in both their genes and their lifestyle."[4]

Another author notes that Okinawa "has gained international recognition for having the highest prevalence of centenarians (people aged 100 years or over) in the world. The average prevalence of centenarians in high-income countries is approximately 10-20 per 100,000, whereas in Okinawa, the prevalence of centenarians is 40-50 per 100,000...The life expectancy in

---

[3]   John Robbins, *Healthy at 100: How You Can--At Any Age--Dramatically Increase Your Life Span and Your Health Span*, New York: Ballantine Books, 2007, 68.

[4]   David Robson, "A High-carb Diet May Explain Why Okinawans Live So Long." BBC Future, January 17, 2019. https://www.bbc.com/future/article/20190116-a-high-carb-diet-may-explain-why-okinawans-live-so-long.

Japan overall is the highest in the world, and the Japanese prefecture of Okinawa ranks first for not only life expectancy, but also quality of life."[5]

Are the claims true about long life in Okinawa?

Catenacci further notes: "Further research has revealed through autopsies that at the time of death, Okinawan centenarians were free of common age-associated diseases like coronary heart disease (CHD), atrophic gastritis, kidney disease, hypertension and metabolic syndromes. Alzheimer's and other neurodegenerative disorders are unheard of in Okinawa. "The most common cause of death in Okinawa is infectious disease, such as pneumonia, rather that the aforementioned chronic diseases that plague the elderly populations of most high-income countries. Studies have shown that when Okinawans migrate, their health and longevity resembles that of their new population."[6]

You may be thinking of other places you thought held the title for producing the oldest people in the world. Perhaps sites come to mind such as the former Soviet state of Georgia, the valley of Vicalbamba in Ecuador, and the Hunza Valley in Pakistan.

However, researchers have found that while some places have boasted of their claims of long lives among their citizens, under scrutiny of providing verifiable proof, it turned out that people sometimes exaggerated their ages, did not have birth records that could be tracked down, or in some cases, did not keep them. When it comes to Okinawa, current and longitudinal data give scientists, researchers, and medical experts the information to verify Okinawa's position of producing the highest prevalence of healthy and old people.

Show me the numbers: Why Okinawa is the place people live the longest and are the healthiest on earth

Since 1879, all villages, towns and cities in Okinawa have kept a family registry system called the *koseki*. This system keeps track of reliable birth,

5   Jocelyn Catenacci, "The Mountain of Youth: What We Can Learn from Okinawa, Japan," *Juxtaposition* Global Health Magazine, University of Toronto, April 2, 2018. https://juxtamagazine.org/2018/04/02/the-mountain-of-youth-what-we-can-learn-from-okinawa-japan/

6   Catenacci, "The Mountain of Youth."

death, and marriage statistics. Data from this system indicate some of the world's highest concentrations of centenarians and super-centenarians.

Reputable organizations such as the Japanese Annual Centenarian report have validated the accuracy of the data from the *koseki* registration system and have found few instances of ages being overestimated.

Here are some opinions from several renowned medical experts, scientists, and researchers about the claim that Okinawans are the healthiest and longest living people in the world.

The Okinawan Centenarian Study

If you are genuinely interested in learning more about scientific and medical research on centenarians, I would suggest beginning with The Okinawa Centenarian Study, a classic longitudinal study on health longevity.

Here is what the three esteemed authors had to say about their goal in conducting this classic and revered study:

> "Our participation in the Okinawa Centenarian Study always had one major goal: to unlock the biological and psychospiritual connections responsible for the everlasting health of the Okinawan elders, preserve the old ways—the Okinawan way—and bring it to the West before it was lost forever…We offer you the common links in wellness and healing that work for thousands of Okinawans, and that we believe will work for you. Our aim is to put you on the path to everlasting health—to help you find your own personal Shangri-La."[7]

The Okinawan Centenarian Study began in 1976 and has been conducted by Japan's Ministry of Health. Data from over 900 Okinawan centenarians has been collected using methodical screening and meticulous documentation. The researchers gathered and carefully examined the information of elderly

---

[7]   Makoto Suzuki, Bradley J. Willcox, and D. Craig Willcox, *The Okinawa Program: Learn the Secrets to Healthy Longevity* (New York: Three Rivers Press, 2001), 9-10.

people in Okinawa via scientific and medical lenses. This has included not just questionnaires from participants but also physical and mental assessments of participants. Their bottom-line findings are as follows:

> "Most older Americans are in far less robust health. When Okinawans do pass on – at the impressive *average* age of almost eight-six years for women and seventy-eight for men (another world record) – it is often classified as old age because no discernable cause can be found, despite autopsy examination."[8]

Another reason I wrote this book did not cross my mind until I had embarked upon my research for this book. I talked to just about anyone who would listen about my book and the incredible knowledge I learned about healthy aging.

Through major medical, research and scientific (MRS) studies, we know exactly what causes and prevents aging. While nothing can completely obliterate aging, there are steps one can take to slow it down. The question, then, is what do the world's best researchers, scientists and medical minds have in their arsenal to help us decipher what proven ways are best to accomplish that feat? In the pages ahead, you will learn proven ways to help ease up on the age accelerator pedal of your life.

I felt it important that the information you will learn not be stated in lofty terms. Therefore, I will translate some overly complex data into simple terms. My goal in writing this book was to summarize what MRS experts have to say about aging as it relates to the healthiest and longest-living people in Okinawa and the "Blue Zones." By the end of this book, you will have a clearer idea about what people do to grow old gracefully and stay healthy during the sunset years of their lives.

Throughout the process of writing this book, many people asked me the same basic questions about aging. I decided to create a Frequently Asked Questions section, which appears in the next chapter.

---

[8]   Makoto Suzuki et al., *The Okinawa Program*, 5-6.

CHAPTER 2:

Frequently Asked Questions (FAQs) About Aging

Have you ever thought about questions like "how long can I expect to live?"

A s we start our journey on the road to healthy aging, here are a few frequently asked questions (FAQs) with answers so you better understand about healthy aging around the world.

How long does the average person around the world live?

To understand how long people live around the world. I turned to the knowledge of the World Health Organization (WHO), which works to achieve "Better health for everyone everywhere." They have more than 7,000 people working in 150 country offices, in six regional offices and headquarters in Geneva, Switzerland. This organization may be familiar to you because of their worldwide mission to "combat communicable diseases." Their name surfaces frequently around their efforts to stave off the novel coronavirus (COVID-19).

WHO provided these insights into life expectancy around the world in a report titled, *World Health Statistics Overview 2019: Monitoring Health for the SDGs (Sustainable Development Goals)*. "Health Life Expectancy" is defined as "a measure of the number of years of good health that a newborn" [born in a given year can be expected to achieve in old age]."

WHO offers these statistics relative to the average life expectancy:

- Global life expectancy for children born in 2019 was 74.2 years for females and 69.8 years for males. Women in Japan can expect to live the longest.
- Life expectancy at age 60 is also greater for women than men: 21.9 years versus 19.0. But an individual child's outlook depends on where he or she is born. [9]

I have always been interested in social causes and ways I can help improve the world from my small vantage point. Given that the world's population is aging tremendously, what can be done to improve the quality of life for people as they age everywhere. Everyone in the world shares three things in common. They are that we all:

- Have been born.
- Must die.
- Will not grow younger but older every day of our lives!

As a citizen of the United States, how long can I expect to live?

The US Social Security Administration offers these numbers relative to life expectancy in the United States:

- A man reaching age 65 in 2019 can expect to live on average, until age 84.0.
- A woman turning age 65 in 2019 can expect to live on average, until age 86.5. [10]

---

[9] World Health Organization, *World Health Statistics Overview 2019: Monitoring Health for the SDGs (Sustainable Development Goals)*, (Geneva, Switzerland: World Health Organization, 2019), https://apps.who.int/iris/bitstream/han dle/10665/324835/9789241565707-eng.pdf, 10-12.

[10] United States Social Security Administration. Benefits Planner/Life Expectancy Calculator. https://www.ssa.gov/OACT/population/longevity.html. Accessed December 26, 2019.

And those are just averages. About one out of every four 65-year-olds today will live past age 90, and one out of seven will live past age 95.

Figure 2-1

Average Life Expectancies

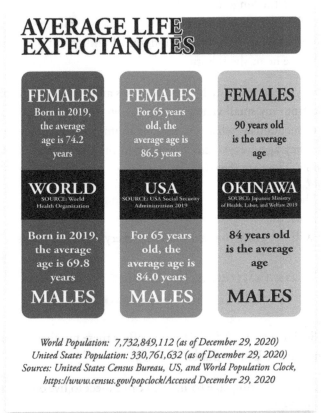

AVERAGE LIFE EXPECTANCIES

FEMALES	FEMALES	FEMALES
Born in 2019, the average age is 74.2 years	For 65 years old, the average age is 86.5 years	90 years old is the average age
WORLD SOURCE: World Health Organization	**USA** SOURCE: USA Social Security Administration 2019	**OKINAWA** SOURCE: Japanese Ministry of Health, Labor, and Welfare 2019
Born in 2019, the average age is 69.8 years	For 65 years old, the average age is 84.0 years	84 years old is the average age
MALES	MALES	MALES

World Population: 7,732,849,112 (as of December 29, 2020)
United States Population: 330,761,632 (as of December 29, 2020)
Sources: United States Census Bureau, US, and World Population Clock,
https://www.census.gov/popclock/Accessed December 29, 2020

Resources to determine your life expectancy

If you want to know your life expectancy, the Social Security Administration has a simple Life Expectancy Calculator that gives a rough estimate of how long you may live. This Life Expectancy Calculator can be found at: www.ssa.gov.

The *True Vitality Test* is offered on www.bluezones.com. As the website explains, this three-minute test "calculates your life expectancy and how long you'll stay healthy. We send you personalized recommendations for getting the most good years out of life. We keep your submissions and results private."[11]

Life expectancy in the USA declines

In every industrialized nation around the world, people are living longer than they did 100 years ago, according to researchers. For example, in 1900 the life expectancy was 47 years old. US population demographics over the past few years, however, have seen some changes which are concerning, especially for working age Americans 25 to 64 years old, who are dying at faster rates than in the past.

An abstract in the prestigious *Journal of the American Medical Association* raises some startling alarms about life expectancy in the US. They examined vital statistics and reviewed the history of changes in US life expectancy mortality rates. They also looked at potential contributing factors and insights from current literature and analyzed state-level trends. As the article states, the bottom line is that:

- US life expectancy has not kept pace with that of other wealthy countries and is now decreasing.
- Between 1959 and 2016, US life expectancy increased from 69.9 years to 78.9 years but declined for 3 consecutive years after 2014.
- By 2014, midlife mortality was increasing across all racial groups, caused by drug overdoses, alcohol abuse, suicides, and a diverse list of organ system diseases.

These startling conclusions indicate that US life expectancy increased for most of the past 60 years, but the rate of increase slowed over time and life expectancy decreased after 2014.[12]

---

[11] "True Vitality Test," Blue Zones, https://www.bluezones.com/live-longer-better/#section-3. Accessed December 26, 2019.

[12] Steven H. Woolf and Heidi Schoomaker, "Life Expectancy and Mortality Rates in the United States, 1959-2017" *JAMA (Journal of the American Medical Association)* 322(20) (November 26, 2019): 1996-2016. doi:10.1001/jama.2019.16932.

Are people 65 and older the fastest-growing segment of the population worldwide?

To understand worldwide aging, it is important to examine population growth dynamics. Research shows that in numerous global locations, people aged 65 and beyond make up the fastest-growing segments of their populations. In some countries like the United States and Japan, there have been declines in fertility (birth) rates. Simply said, there are more old people than younger people. There are other never-before-seen phenomena regarding the aging population. For example, "for the first time in U. S. history, older adults are projected to outnumber children by 2034."[13]

Places already adapting to global aging

The increase of people aged 65 and above is an equal-opportunity occurrence and exists in both poor and wealthy countries. There are, however, places that are experiencing dramatic increases sooner than later. For example, Japan, Europe, and North America are in the forefront of this trend. An October 31, 2019, article in the *New England Journal of Medicine* reports that: "By 2050, the United Nations estimates that older people will constitute more than one third of the population in Europe; approximately one quarter in North America, Latin America, the Caribbean, Asia and Oceania and 9% in Africa."[14]

Countries in Asia and Europe are already experiencing this aging phenomenon and have had to adjust this demanding population. It should be noted that the population in Africa is experiencing a different phenomenon, as reported in an article by the US Census Bureau: "Because of high fertility rates leading to a young age structure, population projections indicate that

---

[13] United States Census Bureau: Stats for Stories, "National Senior Citizens Day," August 21, 2019. https://www.census.gov/newsroom/stories/2019/senior-citizens.html.

[14] Victor J. Dzau, Sharon K. Inouye, Elizabeth Finkelman, John W. Rowe, and Tadataka Yamada, "Enabling Healthful Aging for All: The National Academy of Medicine Grand Challenge in Healthy Longevity." *The New England Journal of Medicine,* 381 (October 31, 2019): 1699-1701. doi:10.1056/NEjMp1912298.

Africa will remain relatively young compared to other regions-even while the African older population nearly quadruples from 40.6 million in 2015 to 150.5 million in 2050."[15]

Japan confronting aging challenges

Because the population in Japan has increased for a while, they are at the forefront of confronting societal aging issues. "Japan, whose over 65 population reached 21% in 2006, has made substantial investments in robotics, artificial intelligence, and other innovations to meet these needs."[16]

Aging and burgeoning healthcare costs

The increasing population of elderly people is wreaking havoc on healthcare systems, not just in the United States but around the world. Often older individuals acquire several chronic diseases, which have helped healthcare costs to burgeon. Aging is a major risk factor for multiple chronic diseases, including "… cancers and cardiovascular and neurodegenerative conditions such as Alzheimer's and Parkinson's diseases, all of which require long-term care."[17]

As a person ages, so does their risk of falling ill to a plethora of debilitating diseases such as:

- Alzheimer's
- Arthritis
- Cancer
- COVID-19
- Dementia
- Depression and Anxiety

---

[15]   Andrew W. Roberts, Stella U. Ogunwoke, Laura Blakeslee, and Megan A. Rabe, *The Population 65 and Older in the United States: 2016.* American Community Survey Reports (ACS-38), United States Census Bureau. October 2018. https://www.census.gov/content/dam/Census/library/publications/2018/acs/ACS-38.pdf.

[16]   Victor J. Dzau et al., "Enabling Healthful Aging for All," 2019.

[17]   Dzau et al., "Enabling Healthful Aging for All," 2019.

- Diabetes
- Heart Disease
- Low Vision
- Macular Degeneration
- Sexual Dysfunction
- Strokes

The issue at hand is how to provide quality healthcare to people throughout their lifespans to increase healthy longevity and thereby reduce outrageous medical costs.

The billion-dollar question: what role do genes and my relatives/ancestors play in me having a long life?

Throughout the writing of this book, I had numerous conversations with people about the roles that genes/relatives/ancestors play in living long and healthy lives.

A common theme was that many thought their ability to live a long life was determined by one main factor: their genes. They would often reflect on their own backgrounds and elaborate about relatives who lived an extra-long, or super-short life.

Invariably, that individual would often make a remark about an extended family member (mother, father or grandparents are typically cited). They would say something like: "You know, I come from a family that lives long lives. My mom died at age 95 and her dad at age 92." More dialogue usually followed, as they wondered out loud about their chances of surviving the ravages of old age. At this point in the conversation, many routinely asked me: "Well, what do my family's genes have to do with how long I will live?"

Rather than immediately answer their question, I would turn the tables and ask them about what they thought. Before I reveal the answer that the experts provide, I would like you to try answering this billion-dollar question by supplying your answer to this question:

What percentage of living a long life is attributed to your heredity, genes/ancestors? (Check your answer)

a. 10%
b. 20%
c. 25%
d. 33%
e. 50%
f. 10-50%
g. All the above

**The answer is G, All the above. Sound confusing? It
is puzzling. Back to my story. I will explain.**

About this point in the conversation on aging, the person became silent for a second, then blurted out, "Well, do you think I will die at an old age like my relatives?" After politely telling them that unfortunately I am not a psychic or able to look with certainty into the future, I then would talk about what the MRS experts have to say. Here is a brief version of my explanation that is based on healthy aging gurus' facts about the role genes play in the healthy aging process.

If your relatives/ancestors lived to an old age (barring unforeseen catastrophes), you have a higher probability of growing old like them than someone whose relatives tended to die at younger ages. The absolute truth is that according to researchers:

**If your ancestors lived long lives, that factor does
increase the chance that you will also live longer,
but perhaps not by as much as you might think.**

Exactly how much do your genes impact your longevity? There is not consensus on this issue. Interestingly, some studies say that your genes only have a slight impact on your life expectancy and that the lifestyle and the environment in which you live have the greatest influence on obtaining a longer lifespan. The studies that I examined estimated ranges of a 10-50% chance that genes in fact were long-life influencers. Several experts, however, claimed that about 25-33% of longevity is due to the genes you inherited from your family.

Danish Twins Study on general health in the elderly

This famous landmark study was first published on February 1, 1991, is often cited. The objective of this research was to look at the influence of environmental and genetic factors on hospitalization and health patterns of elderly people. Seventy-seven percent of 3,099 Danish twins aged 75 years and older as identified via the Danish twin register were interviewed. They also studied, by way of a register linkage, the total number of hospitalizations in 18 years of the entire population, including non-responders.

They found through structural equation modeling that about 25% of the self-reported health and hospitalizations could be attributed to genetic factors while the remainder was likely to have been contributed by non-familial environments. The conclusion was that the variations in general health of elderly could partially be due to genetic factors.

What impact do lifestyle and environment have on healthy longevity?

Here is what the esteemed authors of one of the most prominent longevity studies had to say about this topic in their book, *The Okinawa Program:* "Today's research suggests that while genes contribute to up to one-third of the diseases of premature aging, we are responsible for the other two-thirds."[18] These respected researchers state that healthy lifestyle determinants include:

- Diet
- Regular exercise
- Moderate alcohol use
- Avoidance of smoking
- Blood pressure control
- Stress-minimizing psycho-spiritual outlook

---

[18] Makoto Suzuki, Bradley J. Willcox, and D. Craig Willcox. *The Okinawa Program: Learn the Secrets to Healthy Longevity* (New York: Three Rivers Press, 2001).

Throughout my research, I found that many prominent MRS experts echoed this sentiment:

> "Lifestyle and environment are the major factors
> which contribute to healthy longevity!"

If my parents died at old ages, does that mean that I will probably die old?

The Framingham Study, the Alameda County Study, and the "Termite" Study are famous research studies that focused on examining the age of parents' deaths to determine if it successfully predicted how long their offspring would live relative to their parents' ages. The findings showed that it did, but with only a meager six percent correlation between the lifespan of the parents and that of their offspring.

Who is the oldest person to have ever lived?

While the Bible says that Methuselah lived to be 969 years old, today a person's age must be authenticated and verified via official records like original birth certificates or listings in an official census to be conferred with the title of the "oldest person." Reputable organizations and scientific and medical researchers go to great lengths to verify age statistics. Fully authenticating a person's age may require extensive research through credible and legitimate records and even the utilization of experts in the gerontology field.

The oldest documented and verified person to ever live is Frenchwoman Jeanne Louise Calment. She was born in Arles, France, on February 21, 1875, and died there on August 4, 1997, in a retirement home. When she died of natural causes, Calment was 122 years and 164 days old. She was born fifteen years before the Eiffel Tower was built in Paris and one year after Alexander Graham Bell got a patent for the telephone. She lived a highly publicized and active life. Numerous medical and scientific studies documented her health and lifestyle.

She was married for 46 years to a wealthy distant cousin, Fernand Calment, and had one daughter, Yvonne, and one grandchild, Frederic. She outlived all of them. While she smoked until two years before her death, she felt it was time to quit doing so when she could not light her own cigarette and refused to have someone else do that for her. Like many centenarians and supercentenarians, she led a highly active life and constantly learned new things. At age 85, she took up fencing and was still riding her bike at age 100.

In celebration of her 121ˢᵗ birthday, she recorded a rap song and other tunes for a CD titled *Time's Mistress* on which she reminisced. During her long life, she played the piano, hiked, swam, played tennis, roller skated, and hunted. Some called her a socialite.

When asked about her secret to a long life, she mentioned port wine, her olive oil diet (she also used it on her skin,) having a sense of humor and laughing often. It is said that she adored chocolate and consumed about two pounds of it a week. Funny how much of what she did to live a healthy life, including eating dark chocolate, has been confirmed by scientific and medical research to contribute to healthy longevity. One of my favorite stories about Calment appeared on the Guinness World Records website:

> "As she was without heirs, in 1965 a lawyer named Andre-Francois Raffray set up a 'reverse mortgage' with Jeanne. According to this arrangement, he would pay her 2,500 francs every month until she died, whereupon he would inherit her apartment. It must have seemed like a good deal for Monsieur Raffray (then aged 47)-after all, Jeanne was 90 at the time. Incredibly, however, Jeanne outlived him. He died 30 years later, and his family continued the payments. By the time of her death, they had paid Jeanne more than double the value of her apartment."[19]

While Calment has been dead since 1997, in 2019 a controversy emerged about whether she had lived to 122 years and 164 days. It was spurred by an abstract written by a Russian mathematician, Nikolay Zak. As reported by the *Washington Post*, in his widely circulated document he asserted that

---

[19]   Guinness World Records, "Oldest person ever (female)," https://guinnessworld records.com/world-records/oldest-person-(female)#:~:text=Share &text=The%20greatest%20fully%20authenticated%20age,France%20 on%204%20August%20199. Accessed December 18, 2019.

through his research he had uncovered evidence that seemed to say that when her daughter Yvonne died of pneumonia in 1934 at age 36 that it was really Calment that had succumbed. He contends that her daughter assumed her mother's identity at her death to avoid financial troubles and as part of a tax evasion scheme.[20]

While there have been some claims like Zak's that dispute that Calment was the person who lived the longest, a 2019 article in a special issue of the *Journals of Gerontology Series A: Biological and Medical Sciences* examined this assertion and concluded:

> "In defending the veracity of the well-publicized 122-year life of Frenchwoman Jeanne Calment's age at death… a highly publicized theory challenging Jeanne Calment's age claim was based in part upon the ageist contention that she 'didn't look frail enough to be a supercentenarian.' One of many consistent forms of evidence supporting the claim of a 122-year life is the finding that photos of Jeanne Calment in her tenth and part of her 11th decades of life correlate with real-time descriptions of her remarkable functional status at those ages. Both her appearance and independent function for most of her extremely long life are consistent with what must have been a relatively slow biological process of aging and increased resistance to aging-related diseases and syndromes. This prolongation of good health and function is consistent with James Fries' theory of 'compression of morbidity hypothesis,' which states that as one approaches the limit of life span, long-lived individuals must necessarily compress the period of time in which they experience diseases associated with increased mortality towards the end of their life."[21]

---

[20] Washington Post.com. "French Scientists Stand By World's Oldest Person Jeanne Calment." January 5, 2019. https://www.washingtonpost.com/video/world/french-scientists-stand-by-worlds-oldest-person-jeanne-calment/2019/01/05/c9e46c7a-4964-4869-ae5d-4c305ff5d2bc_video.html

[21] Thomas J. Perls and Erwin J. Tan. "Healthy Longevity: An Introduction to the Series," *The Journals of Gerontolgy, Series A, Issue Supplement 1 Volume 74* (November 13, 2019): S1-3. doi.org/10.1093/gerona/glz237.

Who is the oldest man to have ever lived?

The oldest man to have ever lived was Jiroemon Kimura of the Kyoto Prefecture of Japan. He was born on April 19, 1897, and died on June 13, 2013. He lived 116 years and 54 days, worked as a postman and fathered five children.[22]

Who is the oldest person living as of the writing of this book?

The oldest person living today at this writing is Kane Tanaka of Fukoka, Japan. On June 19, 2021, she was verified as having lived 118 years and 168 days. According to Guinness World Records, Ms. Tanaka was born on January 2, 1903, the same year that aviation pioneers Orville and Wilbur Wright flew the first sustained, powered, and controlled aircraft on December 17, 1903, from Kitty Hawk, North Carolina. [23]

Ask yourself: Would I *really* want to live to be 110 or 122 years old?

Quality of life issues due to declining health also emerge as one grows older. Several people told me that they just would not want to live to be a centenarian if it meant they were unable to perform normal daily activities such as walking, talking, or breathing on their own. They expressed no desire to stay alive if every day they were in pain, miserable, and had watched almost all their friends and family die. While I understand what they are saying, I like to think about it this way: What can I do now so I can be healthy and live a long life later? How can I influence others I love and care about to also consider ways to stay young and healthy while growing older?

---

[22] Masakazu Senda, "World's oldest person confirmed as 116-year-old Kane Tanaka from Japan." https://www.guinessworldrecords.com/news/2019/3/worlds-oldest-person-confirmed-as-116-year-old-kane-tanaka-from-japan/. Accessed December 27, 2019.

[23] M. Senda, "World's oldest person confirmed…" 2019.

Many times, throughout the writing of this book, I had to stop and ask myself this very personal question. Do I *really* want to live to be 110 years old or even beyond to surpass Jeanne Calment's 122 year (and 164 days) world record as the Oldest Person to Have Lived?

Answer: (Drum Roll, Please.)

Yes! I would *love* to live to see 110 birthdays or more. Even better, I would not mind trying to beat Jeanne Calment's record. I have a caveat to my answer. I would adore to attempt those feats, but only if I became like the people in Okinawa and the "Blue Zones." By so doing, I would also remain healthy, active, productive and have a reason to wake up *every* morning ready to fulfill my Ikigai (reason for being/sense of purpose)!

After finally reaching an answer to this question, I started to think more deeply about what it would take to accomplish that feat. I began to ponder a deeper question that I wanted to explore by writing this book. This leads me to the next FAQ.

Can the Fountain of Youth be found?

Photo by: Rob Oechsle

The more I conducted research on healthy aging, the more I had to explore what could I do to find that proverbial fountain. I began examining what others have done in the past and present to slow down the aging process.

I found that throughout history, people worldwide have searched for ways to prevent or conquer the dreaded aging process. To accomplish this, they have explored a plethora of approaches to overcome old age. Some have tried taking pills, drugs, and elixirs while others searched for an antidote, a way of life, or any means necessary to delay the inevitable fact that someday their youth would be taken away and replaced by a deterioration of their minds and bodies. Fortunes have been made by smooth-talking companies peddling their claims about reversing the aging process. In all honesty, medical and scientific communities have also participated in the anti-aging money-making game.

People determined to turn back time have traversed the world to discover places that may have already found the secrets to stalling old age. Some have scoured the earth looking for that magical spot that could stop them from aging. Legend has it that in 1513, the adventurous explorer Ponce de Leon ventured from his homeland of Spain to Florida in hopes of finding and drinking from the fountain of youth that magically would allow him to live forever on earth.

Books, musicals, movies, and plays have been written about the dream of discovering a real-life place called Shangri-La, that unique place where people not only lived to infinity and beyond but possessed wisdom about how to have a wildly happy, healthy, and prosperous eternal life. So, who or what should one believe relative to what does in fact work to delay time's mind and body deterioration tactics?

Because so many people are dispensers of fake information about magic potions to prevent aging, efforts have been made by some to put an end to them. In the second edition of his book, *The Blue Zones,* revered longevity expert, researcher, and author Dan Buettner discussed one such initiative by demographer S. Jay Olshansky.

"Squashing Fountain of Youth Charlatans Forever"

S. Jay Olshansky of the University of Illinois at Chicago and more than 50 leading longevity experts published a position statement to "Squash Fountain of Youth charlatans forever." It said:

"Our language on this matter must be unambiguous," they wrote. "There are no lifestyle changes, surgical procedures, vitamins, antioxidants, hormones, or techniques of genetic engineering available today that have been demonstrated to influence the process of aging. The brutal reality about aging is that it has only an accelerator pedal. We have yet to discover whether a brake exists for people. The name of the game is to keep from pushing the accelerator pedal so hard that we speed the aging process."[24]

Where do the healthiest and longest living people on earth live?

This last FAQ is one that I thought a lot about while writing this book. I learned that a ton of scientific and medical research has been done to answer this question. I then discovered that researchers had pinpointed the exact sites where healthy longevity rules. These places are called the "Blue Zones."

If you thought that Okinawa is the only place where people are healthy and live the longest, you will learn in the next chapter about the "Blue Zones" that there are four other places in the world where the healthiest and longest-living people also reside. Now that you know why I felt the need to write a book about healthy longevity and have discovered the answers to several FAQs about aging, I want to tell you about places in the world that are centers of excellence for healthy aging.

Okinawa and four other destinations are called the "Blue Zones." These are the five places that have been "scientifically certified" as producing the people who live the longest and are the healthiest on earth. Let us explore more about the "Blue Zones" in the next chapter.

---

24   Dan Buettner, *The Blue Zones: Second Edition. 9 Lessons for Living Longer from the people who've lived the longest* (Washington, DC: National Geographic Society, 2012), 24.

CHAPTER 3:

"Blue Zones": Five Places Where People Live the Longest and Healthiest on Earth

Introducing the Godfather of the "Blue Zones"

The best way to explain what are the "Blue Zones" is to introduce you to a world-renowned MRS healthy aging expert, Dan Buettner, who I call the "Godfather of the 'Blue Zones.'" I have the upmost respect for his work and have learned volumes from his research. Buettner is a revered National Geographic Fellow, researcher, activist, explorer, educator, journalist, speaker, and *New York Times* bestselling author of several books including:

- *The Blue Zones: 9 Lessons for Living Longer From the People Who've Lived the Longest*
- *Thrive: Finding Happiness the Blue Zones Way*
- *The Blue Zones Solution*
- *The Blue Zones of Happiness: Lessons From the World's Happiest People*
- *The Blue Zones Kitchen: 100 Recipes to Live to 100*

Buettner has traveled the world studying, researching, and documenting information about the people who live the longest and are the healthiest in the world. He and other researchers have pinpointed five areas called the "Blue Zones." These locations share nine common healthy aging traits that he calls the Power 9.

"Blue Zones" history

The term "Blue Zones" was originally based on demographic work by Gianni Pes and Michael Poulain. Their research focused on identifying places with huge percentages of individuals who lived long and healthy lives. They discovered that the largest number of male centenarians in the world was on the island of Sardinia in the Nuoro province of Italy. On a map, this pair drew concentric circles in blue ink to identify the actual villages where the greatest percentage of people were healthy and lived the longest. They dubbed the areas inside the blue circles, "Blue Zones." Thus, the term was born! Their work was featured in the *Journal of Experimental Gerontology.*[25]

As a National Geographic Fellow and researcher, Buettner collaborated with National Geographic to assemble some of the world's most highly regarded longevity researchers and experts. In 2005, *National Geographic* magazine published a landmark cover story titled, "The Secrets of Long Life." In it, Buettner revealed his data and anecdotal observations about the places where people have achieved healthy longevity. [26]

Buettner spent over ten years locating those areas around the globe with unusually high concentrations of one-hundred-year-old people who lived long without acquiring diseases such as cancer, diabetes, heart problems, and obesity. Demographer Michael Poulain eventually teamed up with Buettner. Poulain's expansive research and data analysis helped to identify more sites with people living long and healthy lives.

To further validate their research, Buettner and colleagues traveled to the identified locations to verify and authenticate the ages of the individuals they studied by examining birth certificates and death records. Reputable researchers studying human longevity are compelled to take these steps

---

[25]   Michael Poulain, Gianni Pes, C. Grasland, C. Carru, L. Ferucci, G. Baggio, C. Franceschi, and L. Deiana. (2004), "Identification of a Geographic Area Characterized by Extreme Longevity in the Sardinia Island: The AKEA Study." *Experimental Gerontology* 39 (9) (2004): 1423-1429. doi.org/10.1016/j.exger.2004.06.016.

[26]   Dan Buettner, "The Secrets of Living Longer." *National Geographic* (November 2005), 2-27.

to fully authenticate claims of ages as it has been found that sometimes individuals either exaggerate or simply do not know their true ages. Buettner states that once they finished identifying the five places, he broadened his team to include a cross-disciplinary group of:

- Anthropologists
- Demographers
- Epidemiologists and
- Medical researchers

Their goal was to search and determine if there were "evidence-based common denominators among all places." They hit the jackpot, because they found that there was not one, but *nine* common denominators. Buettner and his team composed working theories and traveled more than twenty times to the "Blue Zones." They collaborated with local researchers and experts studying centenarians. They "interviewed a representative sample of 90- and 100-year-olds as well and cross-checked their work with academic papers. In addition to the quantitative research, they also conducted qualitative research. Buettner explains:

> "I found it especially helpful during my 20 or so trips to the Blue Zones to spend time just sitting with 100-year-olds and listening to their stories and paying attention to their lives. I watched as they prepared their meals, and I ate when and what they were used to eating. I knew that these people were doing something right—it was not just that they had won the genetic lottery. But what was it?"[27]

Where are the "Blue Zones"?

Buettner and his international colleagues located what he calls "pockets of people around the world with the highest life expectancy, or with the highest proportions of people who reach age 100 and are healthy." Backed up by their rigorous scientific inquiry, in 2009, they were ready to reveal the places in the world that met their criteria cited above. They identified their original five "Blue Zone" locations that met their criteria. They are:

---

[27] Dan Buettner, *Blue Zones Solutions: Eating and Living Like the World's Healthiest People* (Washington, DC: National Geographic Society, 2015), 19.

- **Ogliastra Region, Sardinia** – Located in the mountain highlands of this Mediterranean country, it boasts the highest percentage of 100-year-old males.

- **Ikaria (also spelled Icaria), Greece** – Residents of this Aegean Island practice the Mediterranean diet and have the lowest rates of dementia and middle-aged mortality.

- **Nicoya Peninsula, Costa Rica** – In this idyllic tropical paradise, people have low middle-aged mortality. It also has the second-highest numbers of male centenarians.

- **Seventh-day Adventists in Loma Linda, California** – The Seventh-day Adventist community in Loma Linda, California, is home to people who outlive their North American compadres by ten years.

- **Okinawa, Japan** – While the Japanese in general live long lives, the Okinawans for decades have been crowned the worldwide title holders for healthy longevity. Females on this island are the longest-living women on earth.[28]

Figure 3-1-World Map of Blue Zones Locations

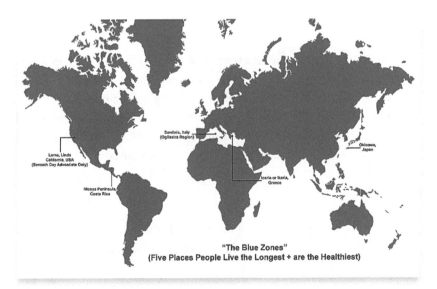

"The Blue Zones"
(Five Places People Live the Longest + are the Healthiest)

---

[28]   Buettner, *Blue Zones Solutions*, 19.

Power 9: Common principles
practiced in ALL "Blue Zones"

Buettner's "Power 9" model delineates nine common principles practiced by the "Blue Zones" people. As you will see later, my model called *MRAF's "8 Healthy Longevity Principles,"* incorporates Buettner's information, plus adds additional dimensions from other world-renowned MRS experts. The Power 9 common practices of the five "Blue Zones" are:

1. Move Naturally
2. Purpose
3. Downshift
4. 80 Percent Rule
5. Plant Slant
6. Wine @ 5
7. Right Tribe
8. Community
9. Loved Ones First[29]

A brief description of these nine powerful longevity principles appears below.

1. Move Naturally

Staying active via natural means is what people who live long lives practice. Moving naturally includes creating a lifestyle and environment full of physical activity. Individuals stay fit by walking up the stairs rather than taking an elevator, gardening, and performing chores like housework and yard work. These activities become routine and provide an excellent way to exercise. A bonus is that they are free or cost little money.

2. Purpose

Knowing one's purpose creates a life that is fulfilling. According to Dan Buettner, It can also add an additional seven years to your life expectancy.

---

[29] Buettner, *Blue Zones Solutions*, 20-21

3. Downshift

Those who live the longest have found ways to minimize or prevent stress that leads to chronic diseases. They routinely "downshift" and take a break from hectic work schedules and other stressors. This can range from keeping a gratitude journal to meditating or taking a siesta or power nap.

4. 80 Percent Rule

Over indulging leads to weight gain. Obesity kills. After eating, it takes 20 minutes for the stomach's "stretch" receptors to notify the brain that hunger no longer exists. To prevent overeating, people must stop eating when they feel 80%, not 100%, full.

5. Plant Slant

A plant-based diet including plenty of beans, lentils and leafy green vegetables are key to healthy aging. Small amounts of meat, even pork, can be eaten, but in moderation.

6. Wine @ 5

Except for one of the Blue Zones (the Seventh-day Adventists in Loma Linda, California), people drink one or two glasses of an alcoholic beverage daily in the evening around five o'clock when work ends. They imbibe in the company of loved ones, family, or friends. This activity connects them to their support network and lets them leave behind the worries of work (or in the COVID-19 era, at the home office).

7. Right Tribe

Creating social circles and environments that help support healthy living behaviors is of utmost importance. People who live the longest work hard to design a life within a "Right Tribe." They also maintain positive relationships with friends and understand the positive and negative impact of people in their lives.

8. Community

Many who live long lives are members of some faith-based or religious community. They are also active in their spiritual pursuits. Dan Buettner reports that individuals who participate in faith-based activities at least four times per month can add from four to fourteen years onto their lives.

9. Loved Ones First

Family relationships are extremely important to individuals who are centenarians. They put family first. Dan Buettner explains that individuals who have a life partner or are married also can add an additional three years of life expectancy.

Dan Buettner offers a compelling reason why you should consider adapting a lifestyle which incorporates the Power 9:

> "… most of us have the capacity to make it well into our early 90s and largely without chronic disease. As the Adventists demonstrate, the average person's life expectancy could increase by 10-12 years by adopting a Blue Zones lifestyle."[30]

Today, Buettner continues his landmark work and is also the founder of the Blue Zones and Blue Zones, LLC. He also has established the popular websites **www.bluezones.com** and **www.bluezonesproject. com**. In addition, his Blue Zones Project has partnered with the American Association of Retired Persons (AARP), the United Health Foundation, and others to help transform cities by applying his principles from the Power 9.

In the next chapter, you will learn more about my favorite "Blue Zone", Okinawa. I will share my memories of growing up there and discuss why *so* many call it Shangri-La and "The Land of the Immortals."

---

[30] Dan Buettner, "Power 9," Blue Zones, https://www.bluezones.com/2016/11/power-9/ (Accessed April 18, 2018).

CHAPTER 4:

Visit to Okinawa: #1 Place People Live to 110+ Years and Are Healthy!

Photo by: Rob Oechsle

"At seventy you are but a child, at eighty you are merely a youth, and at ninety if the ancestors invite you into heaven, ask them to wait until you are one hundred... and then you might consider it."

-Words etched into this welcome marker near the beach at Ogimi, a village in Northern Okinawa.

Okinawa has been a part of my life since I first lived on the island some 60 years ago in 1961. The first part of my book's title is "The Okinawa in Me." Why? Because even after leaving that Shangri-La-like place, the powerful "Okinawan Spirit" remained a potent force throughout my life. The positive and memorable lessons I learned there are embedded within my soul to infinity and beyond. As you will discover in the pages ahead, with a little work, the Okinawan spirit of health and longevity can also be found within you.

Photo by: Rob Oechsle
Northern Okinawa Beach

Have you heard of Okinawa?

When I returned home to Boston after my first trip back to Okinawa in 52 years, I spoke to anyone who would listen about Okinawan healthy longevity. Often in the US, when I have such a conversation, only a few people even know where it is located. Those who did, typically said something like, "Isn't that the place where all those people got killed in World War II?" My reply was, "Yes," followed by: "Do you know where people live the oldest and are the healthiest in the world?"

I have been amazed that only about one percent of those I spoke with knew that the answer is Okinawa and that it has a long and rich legacy of healthy aging. So, if you did not know about Okinawa and its longevity reputation, you are not alone.

In contrast, when I converse with people from Asia, many of them know about Okinawa. They are aware of what happened there in World War II and know of its stellar reputation for healthy longevity.

Where in this world is Okinawa?

Are you wondering, where in the world is this magical mystical place called Okinawa? If so, look at the map below. The island is situated in the East China Sea and about as far east as you can go in the world.

Figure 4-1 Map of Okinawa, Japan, and neighbors

Map of Okinawa, Japan, and neighbors

Okinawa is a prefecture (state) in southern Japan, approximately 1000 miles from Tokyo. It is part of the Ryukyu Islands, which is comprised of hundreds of islands, but very few are habitable. Okinawa is technically an archipelago (group of islands) and spans nearly 463 miles (700 km) of the Pacific Ocean. Its boundaries stretch from the south of the Kagoshima Prefecture of Kyushu, Japan, to slightly east of Taiwan. The island is tiny.

Okinawa is close to 70 miles long and 7 miles across.

Okinawa has a subtropical climate and is sometimes referred to "Japan's Hawaii" because of its nice weather, where temperatures average about 61°F in January and 81°F in July. The subtropical island is full of pristine beaches, lush rain forests, mountains, and an abundance of exotic flora and fauna.

Okinawa has a population of about 1.4 million people. As Fodor's Travel, one of my favorite travel information resources, states, more than 90% of the population "… lives on Okinawa Honto, the largest and most developed island of the chain. Honto is notorious for also housing the bulk of Japan's American military presence, though unless you are visiting a friend in uniform, your focus will be the island's beaches, moving war memorials, natural escapes, and the World Heritage castles and monuments of the Ryukyu Kingdom."[31]

Kadena Air Base and the traditional village where I lived are in Honto. Traveling to Okinawa from the East Coast of the United States where I live is no easy feat. One must pack a huge suitcase filled with patience to endure that journey. During my last trip there, it took me three days to travel from Okinawa back to Boston. It is a *long* distance. Depending on whether it is Daylight Savings Time or Eastern Standard Time in my hometown of Boston, Okinawa's clocks are between 13 and 14 hours ahead.

At some point in the journey to Okinawa, you cross the international date line, which can lead to serious jetlag. Upon reaching this destination, your body cannot decide if you should stay up, go to sleep, or both. Confusion

---

[31] Brett Bull et al., *Fodor's Travel Japan* (New York: Fodor's Travel, a division of Penguin Random House, 2016), 670.

may also occur about what is the correct day of the week. To illustrate my point, on one trip, I was eating my New Year's Day breakfast, on January 1, 2017, at 9 a.m. in Chatan, Okinawa. Back in my hometown of Boston, however, it was still December 31, 2016, at 11 p.m. and friends had not even had the opportunity to take a sip of champagne and scream, "Happy New Year!"

Why is Okinawa called the "Keystone of the Pacific"?

Because of its strategic location in the world, Okinawa is called the "Rock" as well as the "Keystone of the Pacific." I first discovered why Okinawa has that moniker when I attended Kadena Elementary School in Chatan, Okinawa. I learned the meaning of that term from my loved fifth grade teacher, Miss O'Brien. She was a tall, statuesque platinum blonde, reminiscent of Doris Day, a popular movie star at that time. Miss O'Brien told us enthusiastically that we were living in a special place on earth.

She said, "The reason Okinawa is referred to as 'The Keystone of the Pacific' is because it is one of the best locations in the world." She went on to say, "From this wonderful place we can travel very easily and quickly to just about *any* place in the world. We can go to places like our neighbors in China, Taiwan, Guam, the Philippines, India, Australia, New Zealand and even to Russia, Europe and the United States of America!"

The importance of Okinawa's ideal and strategic location in far eastern Asia and the world has been noted throughout time. Historical accounts abound of countries that have viewed it to something akin to a crown jewel.

"Land of the Immortals"

Photo courtesy: Rob Oechsle
Aikwa (Love flower or flowering love) kindergarten in
old Ryukyuan, capital of Shuri, circa 1907

Okinawans are no newcomers to the healthy longevity scene. For centuries, their worldwide reputation for producing what some believe are "Immortal People" (i.e., people who live forever) has been widely known and documented. Ancient Chinese writings dating back some 2,500 years dubbed Okinawa "The Land of the Immortals."

Ancient Chinese search to live forever

Ancient Chinese explorers searched 800 years for the location of Shangri-La in the East China Sea, where it was rumored that people lived forever. Historical documents show they felt that Okinawa in the Ryukyu Islands was that place: "The mysterious Eastern Sea Islands held great interest for the early Chinese dynasties. According to the *Shan Hai Ching*, an ancient historical text, the first emperor, Ch'in Shih Huang Ti (221-210 B.C.), sent several missions into the Eastern Sea in the direction of the Ryukyu Islands to search for the secrets of immortality and for a formula that could turn base metals into gold."[32]

For thousands of years, foreign entities have invaded Okinawa, hoping to conquer and own a piece of this valuable world real estate. Okinawa is in the vicinity of many formidable fighting-machine countries like China, Korea, Taiwan, Russia, India, and Vietnam, to name just a few of the island's neighbors.

It is said that karate was invented in Okinawa so its residents could defend themselves from these foes. After all, these peace-loving people had to find a way to preserve their "heaven on earth."

To understand the magnitude of Okinawa's strategic location, we will look in Chapter 9 at why some of the bloodiest fighting at the end of World War II (WWII) took place there.

Battle of Okinawa April 1- June 22, 1945

As discussed, the ancient Chinese some 2,500 years ago understood the prime real estate value of the "Land of the Immortals." During World War II, countries around the world came to know Okinawa's strategic value as the "Keystone of the Pacific." You may recall that during WW II, the Asia-Pacific portion of the war began with a surprise and deadly attack on Pearl Harbor in Hawaii and an invasion on the Malay Peninsula in 1941. What you may not know is that:

During World War II, the largest amphibious warfare invasion in the Pacific Theater took place in Okinawa, Japan.

According to the *Himeyuri Peace Museum: The Guidebook*, toward the end of WWII in the Pacific theater, close to 200,000 people were killed in Okinawa in just a little more than two months from April 1 to June

---

Makoto Suzuki, Bradley J. Willcox, and D. Craig Willcox, *The Okinawa Program: Learn the Secrets to Healthy Longevity* (New York: Three Rivers Press, 2001), 423.

22, 1945. This figure includes both soldiers and non-combatants.[33] The magnitude of these numbers cannot be dismissed. After all, it is a tiny island (70 miles long and 7 miles across).

Vintage photo courtesy: Donn Cuson
The Battle of Okinawa April 1- June 22, 1945

The enormous number of casualties for such a tiny place included innocent Okinawan women and children along with their teachers and parents. Okinawans endured deplorable and unimaginable conditions. They were subjected to inhumane treatment such as:

- Entire families as well as teachers along with their young innocent students were forced by the Japanese military to commit mass suicide rather than subsist in a war-torn society where dying was a better option than living.
- People surviving on meager meals consisting of cockroaches, rainwater, and, on a good day, a staple diet of purple sweet potatoes (beni imo), a few kernels of rice, wild foods, and berries.

Many escaped but were forced to live in caves deep inside jungles infested with habu snakes, a highly venomous reptile deadlier than cobras. Others sought refuge in remote mountains.

---

[33] Yoshiko Shimabukuro, *Himeyuri Peace Museum: The Guidebook* (Okinawa, Japan: October 2016), 2.

Tips to survive pandemics: Lessons from the Battle of Okinawa

At this point, you might be thinking about some of the same questions that I often pondered. They are:

- Despite the unthinkable hardships Okinawans suffered, how did they manage to bounce back after WWII to the point of becoming the oldest and healthiest-living people on earth? Why were they able to accomplish that impossible feat?
- How can I learn from the Okinawans who survived such inhumane conditions about their secrets of moving from tragedy to triumph and gloom to glee?
- Most importantly, how can I apply their wisdom to my life when I hit tragic and tough times, even like those which occurred during the COVID-19 era?

In the pages ahead, you will be exposed to life lessons from Okinawans on how to battle through those difficult times in life. You will discover the unique ways that many Okinawans employ to combat fatigue from stress and bad times. More importantly, you will learn how to apply this invaluable information to *your* life, especially when you are faced with tragic times.

Despite their horrific experiences, Okinawans eventually emerged stronger. They rebuilt their lives after World War II. How did they accomplish this incredible feat *and* emerge to be winners at healthy aging? I invite you to keep reading as the answers to these big questions and more will be revealed.

Differences between Okinawa and mainland Japan

To really know Okinawa, it is important to understand the differences between the island and mainland Japan. Geographically, Okinawa is a separate island from mainland Japan. Uchina is the local name for Okinawa. While it is now a prefecture (state) of Japan, for much of history it was its own distinct territory. From the fifteenth to the seventeenth century, Okinawa was part of the ancient Ryukyu Kingdom. In 1879, the 600-year reign of the Ryukyu kings ended, and Okinawa became a prefecture of Japan. This lasted until after the Battle of Okinawa and the end of World War II in 1945.

May 15, 1972, Reversion: Okinawa is returned to Japan

As part of a postwar agreement, the island became controlled by the US. When I lived in Okinawa in early 1960, it was not a part of Japan. Okinawa officially became part of Japan when it was returned by the United States in what has been called "The Reversion." On May 15, 1972, Okinawa became a prefecture of Japan. Some people consider themselves Okinawans, not Japanese.

While Japanese enjoy a much higher life expectancy than those residing in the western world, it is Okinawans who possess the "Crown Jewel of the healthy longevity game" and have a greater lifespan than those on the mainland.

Okinawans are culturally and linguistically different from mainland Japanese. They speak their own Ryukyuan languages and, while they share some Japanese grammar and vocabulary, it is uniquely Okinawan. Often, people who speak Japanese find the Ryukyuan languages to be incomprehensible.

The complicated Japanese/Okinawan dynamic

Okinawa's connection with Japan has at times been a difficult one. *Himeyuri Peace Museum: The Guidebook* explains how their relationship was strained during World War II:

> "Okinawa was regarded as a pivotal strategic site for Japan's imperial expansion, and students in Okinawa were taught to increase their self-awareness as Japanese to help Japan's militaristic goals. The students were required not only to study regular school subjects but also abandon Okinawan

language and clothing to be assimilated into standard Japanese culture."[34]

Fodor's says the following about the differences between Okinawa and mainland Japan:

"Naha, Okinawa's capital, is geographically closer to Taiwan than to any of Japan's main islands, but deeper distinctions of culture and history are what really set the islands apart. Okinawa's indigenous population comprises an ethnic group independent from the mainland Japanese, and local pride lays much heavier with Okinawa's bygone Ryukyu Kingdom than it ever will with the Empire of the Rising Sun.

Island culture today forms an identity around its Ryukyu roots but also reflects the centuries of cross-cultural influence brought to Okinawa on successive tides of imperialism. Ships from ancient Polynesia, Ming China, Edo (now Tokyo) and most recently wartime America brought the ravages of conquest and the joys of new traditions (snakeskin instruments, the stir-fry, and Spam). Okinawa's melting pot is sharply different from mainland Japan's commercial culture of appropriation and pastiche, touching every element of island life and lending flavor to the music, language, cuisine, architecture, arts and lifestyle that define the archipelago."[35]

The late Anthony Bourdain (RIP), in one episode of his CNN show, *Anthony Bourdain: Parts Unknown*, offered these insights:

"This is Okinawa. Just south of mainland Japan. For all the relative rigidity of the mainland, Okinawa answers in its own unique way. Do not eat the same thing each day. That is boring. There is even an Okinawan term for it, champuru. Something mixed. Bits borrowed from all

---

[34]   Shimabukuro, *Himeyuri Peace Museum: The Guidebook* (2016), 10.

[35]   Bull et al., *Fodor's Travel Japan* (2016), 670.

over served up for anyone to eat… But [what] most do not know is that Okinawa had only become Japan recently.

That Okinawans did not even consider themselves Japanese or vice-versa. That Okinawans and Japanese consider themselves to be different ethnicities, spoke two different languages and culturally, culinarily and in many other ways looked in different directions. Yet, Okinawans [during World War II] were asked to make the ultimate sacrifice and, they did. That is not just ancient history. It informs the present still.

Okinawa is the largest of over 100 islands making up the Ryukyu islands chain. It is just over 300 miles from the mainland, but worlds apart. Okinawa is different. It is tropical. Clear waters; some of the best beaches in Asia for the decidedly more laid back, less frenetic, self-serious attitude than the mainland. You can feel it. You can see it. It's just different here."[36]

Growing up in Okinawa

I am a child of the 1950s. On one of my milestone birthdays, I received a birthday card that had facts about the year I was born. From it, I learned that a postage stamp was a mere three cents. The president of the United States was a man who had been a distinguished general in World War II named Dwight David Eisenhower. I mentioned those facts to a colleague, and he replied, "*Wow*, you *really* are old!"

I want to share what it was like to grow up in the place where people live the longest and are the healthiest in the world. While I was not born in Okinawa, I spent part of my childhood at Kadena Air Base in Chatan. This exotic island is not just a tourist destination for me. It is my adopted homeland. What I learned as an "Air Force Brat" (I hate that term!) living

---

[36] Anthony Bourdain, *Anthony Bourdain: Parts Unknown*, "Okinawa," Season 6, Episode 4, CNN.

there is permanently tattooed on my heart, and it has impacted my life in so many positive ways for over half a century.

Photo by: Rob Oechsle
Kids Playing at Evening, East China Sea

About my Okinawan home

I am a mega-music lover and whenever I hear the lyrics from the song, "Home," my soul is inspired. The tune is from the classic movie, *The Wiz*, which starred the legendary Diana Ross and the late Michael Jackson. It is an adaptation of the popular movie, *The Wizard of Oz*, which featured a young Judy Garland in the iconic role of Dorothy. When I hear this song, I am instantly reminded of growing up in my home at Kadena Air Base. The ballad from *The Wiz* says, "When I think of home, I think of a place where there's love overflowing…" I was eight years old when my family moved to the island. Initially, I hated living there and missed the life I had left behind in the US. Okinawa was *so* different compared to my previous home in Middletown, Pennsylvania. Eventually, I would adore living in Okinawa.

My early years in Okinawa

Martha's Okinawa Passport Picture, 1961

Martha's Kadena Elementary
School Picture, 1962-1963

Dad's career decision to join US Air Force impacted generations

I feel extremely fortunate to have had a father who was a dedicated career soldier. I often reflect on how in 1954 when he was just a teenager, he took a chance and made a career decision that would impact his life and that of his heirs for generations to come. He joined a new branch of the US Armed Forces, which had begun as part of the Army and became its own separate branch in 1947. It had only been in existence for seven years when he enlisted with Uncle Sam. It was called the United States Air Force. It was such a brave step for him to take, given the newness of his employer.

Around the time he enlisted, he married my mom. A few years after signing up with Uncle Sam, he left his young wife and family (which had expanded to five kids) behind in Middletown, Pennsylvania. He had been assigned a new tour of duty in Kadena Air Base in Chatan, Okinawa.

My father, Leonard Mervin, Sr. at Kadena Air Base in Okinawa and in South Korea

My dad had been raised in the rural southern part of the United States by a single mother. His grandmother also raised him and his brother when, to provide for her family, his hardworking and industrious mom moved east to work in the factories that built things needed for our country to fight in World War II.

The Air Force provided a ticket for my dad to leave a meager life that financially would not permit him to get the college education that he wanted so badly. My dad was a noncommissioned officer (NCO) and an extremely hard worker. He was academically brilliant and, in high school and throughout his life, played a plethora of sports like football, softball, handball, and basketball.

After entering the Air Force, he moved up the ranks before he retired. His job in Okinawa was in the accounting area. He worked a second job at the base's Officers' Club to provide for his large and growing family. When my dad was alive, I thanked him on numerous occasions for the career choice he made. I told him how much I appreciated that his wise decision as a teenager positively impacted the lives of his seven children and his heirs for generations.

In my youth, I became a "citizen of the world." Like a mini Margaret Mead-type cultural anthropologist, I loved exploring and navigating my way around the globe. Living in Okinawa taught me about diversity and inclusion, and how to accept and celebrate cultures different than my own. I learned that there is an awesome world out there to explore that is sometimes vastly different, yet, at times, the same as the one that I had left behind in the US.

My mom took five children to Okinawa by herself in 1961

During the frigid winter of 1961, my mom embarked with five kids from Middletown, Pennsylvania across the international date line to reunite us with our father in Okinawa. The older I get, the more I appreciate the incredible tenacity and courage it took for her to take that journey with five children, especially since she had never traveled outside of the United States.

My siblings and I were the proverbial "Irish twins," ranging in age from a toddler to an eight-year-old. We all were roughly a year or less apart in age. I was eight years old in the second grade when we moved thousands of miles away from the icy temperatures of Middletown (near Hershey, the mega-chocolate candy corporation) to Okinawa, a sunshine-laden island off the southern coast of Japan. Entering this strange and exotic culture was quite a shock to my young body and mind.

Family passport picture for Okinawa 1961

Living in Okinawa 16 years after World War II

I am often asked, "Since you were only 8 to 11 years old when you lived there, did you *really* remember everything you experienced in Okinawa?" My response always is that I have somewhat of an elephant's long memory and *vividly* recall living there. Although I left my beloved Okinawa at age 11, the experience of living in what truly was Shangri-La has stuck inside my soul for my entire life.

Culture shock and people with cone-shaped straw hats

Immediately upon first arriving, I could see that the life I had known in the US would never exist in Okinawa. The climate, people, and even my school were 180 degrees different from anything I had previously experienced. I recall our plane landing in Okinawa after our extremely long and exhausting trip.

I was so elated to finally see my father, who had been away from us for such a long time. He picked us up at a tiny airport in Okinawa and as we exited the building, the sweltering hot temperature slapped me in the face. After the seven members of my family piled into our 1960s car, I realized that I was in a faraway place with strange-sounding words and odd things surrounding me.

Culture shock set in on the ride to my new home. We drove down dirt roads, dodging men with cone-shaped straw hats on their heads, guiding humongous oxen. For some reason, people wearing those cone-shaped hats really captured my attention.

Many of these individuals were carrying two buckets that hung from a large stick that was carefully balanced between their shoulder blades. WOW, what they were carrying did REALLY *stink*! I later learned that these pails were called "honey buckets." They, however, were not carrying honey in those buckets; I was told that the buckets held excrement used to fertilize crops.

Photo courtesy: Donn Cuson   Photo courtesy: Rob Oechsle

Men in cone-shaped hats

To demonstrate how different and strange my new home in Okinawa was compared to what I had left in Pennsylvania, check out these vintage pictures from the collection of a curator par excellence, Donn Cuson. Through his pictures on the next few pages, you can appreciate the curious sights I had to adjust to when I left the airport and headed out to my new home for the first time.

Photos courtesy: Donn Cuson
Okinawan Village Scenes 1960s

Arriving at my new home in an Okinawan village

Another "I can't believe what I'm seeing moment" occurred once our ride from the airport ended and we reached the front door of our modest home. It was tiny and certainly did not look like anything I had ever seen. As we pulled up to our new abode, I spotted a mother and baby lizard scurrying around, obviously frightened by our arrival. I was swimming in sweat by the time we stepped inside our new home, which was not located on Kadena

Air Base, but in a quaint traditional Okinawan village with a long dirt road that ended at the edge of the East China Sea.

When I saw the picture of Morgan Manor from Donn Cuson's collection (available to view online at **www.rememberingokinawa**), my first thought was, "Oh my goodness, it looks like the house my family lived in when I first moved to Okinawa!" We lived in this rural village because we had to, as they said, "Wait to move on base." What that meant was that until my dad received the green light for us to reside directly on Kadena Air Base, this quaint village house would be "home sweet home" for our family of five kids and two adults.

This house in an Okinawan Village looks like the home where I lived

Photo courtesy: Donn Cuson
Morgan Manor Dependent Housing Area, 1962

Adjusting to hot dog sukiyaki and an Okinawan village

I cannot minimize how difficult the first few weeks were for me as I adjusted to this strange and exotic location. I had to absorb and understand so many new sights, sounds, and smells that overwhelmed my senses.

It was tough. I missed my friends, school, house, cold winter weather, and the life that I had left behind. While I detest cold weather, I found myself longing to see a snowflake or two. My dad was incredibly good helping us become acclimated to our new home and environment. He was a fabulous cook and tried making different foods that were influenced by Okinawan culture. Some of what he made was amazingly delicious. Other things were just not pleasing to my palate.

I will never forget one dish that he concocted. He called it "hot dog sukiyaki." Sukiyaki is a Japanese dish that contains beef, vegetables, noodles and a sauce of stock, soy sauce and sugar. Somehow he substituted hot dogs for the beef. Not only did the sukiyaki name sound wacky, but whatever ingredients were in it made all of us deathly ill for days. I will just say that the sukiyaki was sickening!

Learning to LOVE living there

It took me awhile to both mentally and physically settle into my new life in an Okinawan village. I was a super-curious child who loved to learn. Eventually, I stopped fighting the strangeness of the place and started exploring its splendor. As mentioned, I fancy myself as a Margaret Mead-type person who, from a young age, was fascinated with learning about cultures and the people within them. In Okinawa, I had the magnificent opportunity to hone my cultural anthropology and sociology interests. Outside our home, a long dirt road meandered its way to the shore of the East China Sea. I enjoyed standing outside in our front yard and watching fellow villagers walk down the street.

Often, I observed those hardworking Okinawan men with the cone-shaped hats herding huge oxen and other animals. I was fascinated by how they balanced those two buckets with utter precision on a long pole positioned between their slender shoulder blades.

One of my favorite things to do was to walk around my village, exploring the scenery and climbing on huge boulders and running along the sun-glistened sand and turquoise waters of the East China Sea. I would run, darting in and out of the water as the tide moved to and from the sandy beach to the sea.

Photo by: Rob Oechsle
Free Spirit Girl at East China Sea Beach

I have always loved to talk. While I only knew a few Okinawan/Japanese words, I was able to engage and communicate with Okinawan people I would meet along my fun-loving walk. I loved the spirit of the Okinawans I encountered on my trips.

What is the "Okinawan Spirit"?

The Okinawan phrase: "<u>ichariba chode</u>" (e-cha-re-ba-cho-de) sums up the vibrant "**Okinawan Spirit**" and *exactly* what I have experienced about the people of this beautiful island in the sun.

Translation:
"Though we meet, but once, even by chance, we are friends (or like family) for life."

These words express the sentiment that almost everyone you meet (including random, brief encounters) are your friends/family members forever. Ichariba chode illustrates the warm, giving and loving "Okinawan Spirit." I personally experienced this phenomenon as a child and again when I have returned in recent years to visit. As a kid, I had no problem meeting friends of all ages in Okinawa. When I made my super-fun jaunts to the seashore in my tiny village, I constantly met and played games with Okinawan children at the beach.

Despite my limited Okinawan language skills, we managed to communicate perfectly. Friendly villagers encouraged me with kind-looking gestures and words I did not understand. The uber-kind older Okinawan people would invite me to partake of exotic meals with my friends and their multigenerational families. Furnishings were sparse in their super-clean homes. The food was tastefully presented with intricate garnishes.

Food was eaten on low tables where you sat on the floor on traditional tatami mats. This woven straw-like flooring is made from a material called *igusa* or a soft rush plant. The igusa has a distinctive odor, especially when it is newly installed; some liken it to a grassy herbal scent.

In the previous chapter, you learned that those who live long, and healthy lives stay fit by "moving naturally." I always thought it amazing how the elderly grandparents sat on the floors like everyone else in their families. Think about how those 100-year-old Okinawan people, for their entire lives, had to get up and down from the floor to partake of their meals. Who would have known that such action not only helps them to maintain their balance as old age creeps into their bones, but also provides natural exercise that can add years to their lives?

Respect for elders and close-knit family groups

As cited by MRS experts, I witnessed in my own excursions, multiple generations of family members living under one roof. Everyone seemed to get along so well. Doting grandparents kept a watchful eye over younger children at home. School-age children always seemed to be attentive to the needs of their elders and vice-versa. The love and respect shown toward the oldest members of the family was highly visible and palpable.

In cultures where people live long lives, it is not uncommon to find multigenerational families living under one roof. Elders are highly respected, and it is expected that they will be taken care of within the context of the family structure. Many societies where people grow old and healthy, like Okinawa, do not have institutions like nursing homes (or they are not widespread). In many cases, families see it as their obligation to provide comfort and shelter within their home for their elderly relatives and citizens.

These societies are also structured in such a way to support a culture where it is an expectation that people will help each other, especially family members, throughout life. They also have a deep respect for and commitment to individuals who are at both ends of life's continuum. In other words, they believe it is their duty to take care of everyone, but especially children and the elderly.

Photo courtesy: Donn Cuson

I was always impressed by how well-behaved and disciplined the young Okinawan children were back during the early 1960s. I have a vivid memory of watching them walking to school in their crisp and neatly pressed uniforms. They seemed to spend a lot of time studying and doing chores side-by-side with other family members of all generations. Regardless of their age, everyone appeared to possess that "get in the groove and move attitude." You will learn later that this is one principle practiced by those who have mastered healthy longevity.

Open-air marketplaces

With my mom, I would visit the Okinawan stores and open-air markets that looked like those in the photographs.

Photo courtesy: Donn Cuson
Black Market Alley, 1952

Photo courtesy: Donn Cuson
Naha Market, 1952

Transitioning from an Okinawan village to Kadena Air Base

Eventually, my family would move onto Kadena Air Base in Chatan, Okinawa. The transition from off-base housing in a traditional Okinawan village to on-base housing in 1961 was also initially a mega-adjustment. To get on the base, my family had to travel through interesting sights and sounds. Here are historical pictures from the collections of Rob Oechsle and Donn Cuson. They remind me of what the area surrounding Kadena Air Base looked like as my family transitioned from village life to base life.

Photo courtesy: Donn Cuson
Street scene, Okinawa, 1960s

Photo by: Donn Cuson
Naha scene

Photo by: Donn Cuson
Koza street scene 1963

Family portrait Kadena Air Base 1962

These family pictures were taken in our Kadena Air Base backyard, which consisted of a small area of grass that had been mowed. It was surrounded by a thick bamboo-like jungle that we called "the boondocks."

Mom, Dad and Sister Opie (born in Okinawa)

My Quonset hut house

The structure of our humble and modest house was called a "Quonset hut." The picture of this igloo-like metal building with a corrugated roof resembles the Quonset hut that my family lived in on the base. On my first trip back to Okinawa in 2016-2017, I learned that these structures are considered a relic of the past and families are no longer subjected to living in these unusual abodes.

Here are some pictures of Quonset huts that looked like my house.

Photos courtesy: Donn Cuson
Quonset hut like we lived in at Kadena Air Base

Back in the early 1960s, Kadena Air Base did not look like it does today. Certain sections looked like a tropical jungle. Many of us who grew up there felt that it was a place where as kids, we were free to roam and play unencumbered in what looked like a Garden of Eden. We lived in the Jennings section of Kadena Air Base.

Jennings area of Kadena Air Base today

Photo by: Rob Oechsle

> **"Playing in our jungle-like backyard and swinging
> from vines was like being in a Tarzan and Jane
> movie minus their monkey, Cheetah."**

Playing outside in Okinawa was like being in a movie with Tarzan and Jane minus their monkey, Cheetah. These three characters were popular in those days. As a kid, I played nonstop with my friends in the jungle-like areas surrounding our neighborhood.

Photo by: Rob Oechsle

Since we were encouraged to go outside and play, many of us looked forward to outdoor recess time at school. Our playtime activities were super high-tech…*not*! We had low-cost or no-cost homemade simple fun such as swinging on sturdy tree vines like Tarzan and Jane did in our community. (Yes, my body did at one time get on a vine and swing across the sky.)

Photo by: Rob Oechsle
Oku River, Okinawa

You might be thinking, *Did your parents* really *let you roam around on your own like that in a foreign country at eight and nine years old?* The answer is *absolutely, yes!* Remember, this was a different time and place in history, and it was totally acceptable to let kids explore their environment.

While it seems strange today, back then, as a nine-year-old child (the oldest of six children at the time), I was given a lot of responsibility *and* freedom. At age nine I started babysitting for families in the Jennings area where we lived. Families were big during that decade, and I was hired to take care of three, four, and five kids with no problem.

I was also allowed to roam basically wherever I wanted around Kadena Air Base. For example, it was nothing to go by myself down the gigantic hill where we lived and catch a base shuttle bus to the movie theater, choir practice, or Sunday school at the base chapel. Yes, at nine years old, I did those things, as did my peers. After meeting others who have lived in Okinawa, I now realize that others felt the same way about their freedom. While I was allowed — in fact encouraged — to explore my surroundings and try new and different cultural things in the Okinawan environment, I also had to deal with a military culture that enforced some strict rules and regulations. My family always underscored the need to always be respectful of others and to use my manners. My parents drilled in us that we were always to be polite, watch our manners and always be on our best behavior and seek to do an excellent job at whatever we were doing. It was a given that elders were to be respected and, in some cases, not to be questioned.

Photo courtesy: Donn Cuson
Camp Boone kindergarten, late 1960s

This is my recollection of a typical playground during the 1960s in Okinawa. Check out the Quonset hut in the background.

Fostering a let-the-day-take-you-wherever attitude

The environment in Okinawa allowed children to be adventurous and explore the people, places, and things around their world. The laid-back, non-rushed environment emphasized that rushing through time wasn't as important as relaxing and foster the letting-the-day-take-you-wherever attitude that's often a trait of those who live long and healthy lives.

Photo by: Rob Oechsle
Una River, Okinawa. Two boys navigate the flat rock and clumps of Egyptian papyrus.

Today, the concept of "mindfulness" (or achieving a mental state by focusing on the present) is something that experts advocate. Practicing mindfulness requires you to be fully present in each moment and aware of where you are and what you are doing. Research has found that by practicing mindfulness, individuals can reduce stress and do not become overwhelmed or overly reactive to the world around them.

I directly credit my experience of growing up in Okinawa with teaching me how to be mindful AND curious about cultures and people from around the world. It also taught me about how to be more inclusive of others and realize that some things in foreign lands may be the same or different from American culture and that is perfectly fine.

We had to be observant and aware of dangers in paradise like grenades, land mines, and habu snakes.

My mom instilled in her children that, although we were living in a beautiful, fun Garden of Eden, we had to *always* be observant and aware of our surroundings. I thank her for everything she did to instill this in me and my siblings. For instance, she taught us to be hyper-observant so we would not accidentally step on anything dangerous while in Okinawa. This included the deadly grenades and land mines left behind during WWII that still lurked in the thick bamboo jungle around our house.

When I first moved to Okinawa, it had only been 16 years since WWII had ended in 1945. As mentioned earlier, some of the fiercest fighting in that war had taken place where we lived, and close to 200,000 people died on Okinawan soil. The reality was that some of the land mines and grenades hidden during the war were still live and could kill little children who were only out to play and have fun in Shangri-La.

If that were not enough, we also had to be diligent and watch out for deadly habu snakes. This venomous pit viper is part of a snake family that includes rattlesnakes and cobras. Unfortunately, if you are bitten by one, you could become permanently disabled or even die.

Photos by: Rob Oechsle
Deadly habu snakes

I loved one of the games my mom would play to heighten our sense of awareness. We might be out at a restaurant when she would say, "Close your eyes and don't peek." Then, she would ask us about items in the room and say things like: "What color are the chairs that you're sitting on?" "Are there any green foods on the table?" "Did you see any pictures on the walls?"

This line of questioning was not only fun but also taught us important lessons about paying attention and *always* watching and looking at the world around us.

Recently, on several posts that I saw on one of my favorite Facebook pages called "Yeah... I lived in Okinawa," I read numerous posts where American kids like me recounted similar Okinawan wanderlust stories. As one person put it, "the environment we grew up within Okinawa was an extremely safe and nurturing one."

As you will learn, a positive lifestyle and nurturing environments are some of the main ingredients in the healthy longevity life recipe.

Education and attitude

My parents and teachers at Kadena Elementary School were all incredible educators. They taught me to believe that if I truly put my mind to it, I could solve or do anything in the world. They served as a supportive team that drilled into my brain and soul that my desires and wishes, no matter how big, could be achieved. Further, I was highly encouraged to not just dream but also live my dreams daily. When I had even a slight doubt about exploring my horizons, both my internal home and external military environment would remind me that "Nothing'll stop the US Air Force" *and* if I adopted that philosophy, like the US Air Force, nothing'll stop me!

Okinawa: Where I learned how to love learning

My mother did a magnificent job of reinforcing the notion that it was of utmost importance to study hard and get a good education. Making A and B grades was allowed. Let us just say that achieving C, D, or F grades was not an option. She made learning fun and adored writing on just about any topic. An avid reader, she devoured daily newspapers and loved reading the cartoons out loud as she laughed at their humor.

Role of the sensei (teacher)

In Okinawa, sensei (meaning teacher) as well as the elderly take their role as human vehicles to impart and transfer knowledge seriously. My educational experience in Okinawa taught me how to love learning. I received a fabulous education from caring teachers, such as my favorite fifth grade teacher, Miss O'Brien. She looked as if she could be the beautiful sister of the famous blonde actress Doris Day. Her teaching was intoxicating, and I drank from her glass of education. I loved going to school so much that I did not want to stay at home when I was sick! I know, that is a little nerdy, but it is the truth.

When I was ill and still tried to attend my beloved Kadena Elementary School, my mother would speak in a very stern voice. With her Southern belle-tinged twang, she would say, "Girl, you better get back to bed. School will be there when you're gone." Her "gone" sounded a lot more like *gawhn!* I have never forgotten her oh-so-true words and her Southern street-smart thinking.

My mother, along with both my Okinawan and American teachers, taught me the value and importance of learning.

My mom in 1962, Kadena Air Base, Okinawa.

As I worked on this section of the book on Tuesday, February 4, 2020, I sat in the Newton, Massachusetts, Public Library and thought about how

I do believe that in life there are no coincidences, and everything happens for a reason. On this day, my mother died. She had been on my mind all day. As I sat there making the changes to my manuscript, she was once again influencing my life as I write and reflect about her and growing up in Okinawa.

Thanks, Mom, for all your love and guidance. There is no doubt in my mind that those early childhood lessons she imparted served as the foundation for the educator that I would become and the professions I would choose in life.

I often wonder about what became of my fifth-grade teacher in Okinawa, Miss O'Brien. If she is still alive, she would be incredibly old. I would love her to know how much her dedication as a teacher meant to me and helped shape my life in so many positive ways.

I learned how to be a global citizen when my class studied Okinawan tea ceremonies, kimonos, and island history. We also participated in arts and crafts such as making glass wind chimes and writing our names in Japanese on scrolls.

In 2016, when I went back to Okinawa for the first time, Airman Briana Cotton was my military sponsor and took me on an escorted tour of Kadena Air Base. When I got in the vicinity of my beloved Kadena Elementary School, although it had been 52 years since I had seen it, I immediately knew that I was back on the school's playground.

Looking around at the school, I stepped out of the car and exclaimed over and over to Briana, "I can't believe it. *I am back* at Kadena Elementary School! It looks the same. Oh, my goodness, it looks the same!" To my amazement, almost everything looked pretty much as I had remembered, except that the swings on the playground were pointed in a different direction than I recalled.

On my second trip to Okinawa in 2018, Briana was my military sponsor for a second time and again she drove me by the school. This time when I got out of the car, I noticed that things looked a tad different. I peered inside the windows of the cafeteria and a few classrooms. The classrooms were empty and on a wall were scribbled farewell notes and pictures drawn by previous students. Inside one classroom was a sign that took me by surprise because I remembered that what was printed on the sign was something Miss O'Brien would say. It said:

"How do you know if you haven't tried it!"

As it turned out, a new school had been built and they were in the process of closing my old school. I thought it was fabulous that they allowed the students to place farewell messages and pictures on the outside of some buildings. What many of the kids wrote really shocked me. Why? Because I had had the same thoughts as a student there.

Here is a photo I took of some of their thoughtful messages. Many of them were super-kind words about how much the kids *loved* attending school there.

Photo by: MRAF
Student farewell messages at closing of Kadena Elementary School, 2018.

I did two things before leaving nostalgia behind at the school. First, I hopped on a swing and, soaring as high to the sky as I could, recalled how much fun I had had playing on them at recess in the 1960s. I took a moment to wallow in my great memories of what a great educational experience I received.

Me in 2018 on swings at my old Kadena Elementary School.

After hitting the swings, Briana and I piled into her car. As we began to exit the school grounds, something caught my eye. I asked her to stop the car, so I could take a picture of the sign (see photo), which read: "Educate, Engage and Empower Each Student to Succeed in a Dynamic World."

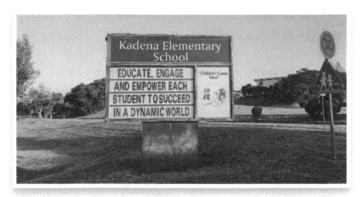

Kadena Elementary sign summarizes how seriously
teachers took their educational responsibility.

I can attest that my teachers and mother absolutely fulfilled the mission of those words because after I left Kadena Elementary School, I was truly ready and was confident in my belief that if I put my mind to it, like the US Air Force, nothing would stop me! Tears welled in my eyes as I read the sign repeatedly. Why? It hit me that the sign described a way of seeing the world that had been instilled in me by the dedicated teachers who had taught me there. The phenomenal, timeless wisdom they bestowed upon me has sustained me throughout my life.

In Okinawa, individuals serving as teachers (sensei) take their educational role super-seriously. They revel and delight in watching their pupils absorb their amazing and bountiful wisdom and use it to achieve in life and at work. It is an honor to watch their subjects advance in their own knowledge, skills, and abilities. They desire, and almost see it as an obligation, to impart their knowledge and wisdom to their heirs and others in the society. Giving back and an attitude of continuous learning helps one achieve healthy longevity.

Research indicates that people who live long and healthy lives approach learning with excitement and welcome the opportunity to increase their knowledge as well as impart it to others. The invaluable gift of loving to learn is a present that was given to me from my experience of living in Okinawa. Little did I know that they had gifted me with one of the secrets to living a long and healthy life. I want to personally thank all my American and Okinawan teachers both past and present for truly leading me to a path where I feel that I obtained their goal for students like me to be empowered "to succeed in a dynamic world!"

Life lessons learned from Okinawa: How to be a citizen of the world

Okinawa prepared me to become a citizen of the world. I took in so many enduring lessons from residing there, including the following.

Underneath my worldly and city-like ways that I enjoy in my hometown of Boston, is an island girl who also adores jungles and rain forests. I feel just as comfortable at a five-star hotel like the Four Seasons in Boston as I have in a thatched hut on the Momon River in the Amazon jungle of Iquitos, Peru or in a village in Negril, Jamaica or Okinawa, Japan. As discussed, I learned at an early age to be very observant and look out for signs of trouble like deadly and venomous habu snakes or leftover grenades and land mines in the backyard jungle we called "Boondocks" outside of the igloo-shaped Quonset hut I lived in on Kadena Air Base.

In school and in daily life, I experienced aspects of culture that had not been a part of my American traditions. These included traditional tea ceremonies and learning how kimonos were worn by beautiful Okinawan women and geishas, as well as taking school field trips to sites like Suicide Cliff (where people were forced by the Japanese military to commit suicide because it seemed like a better alternative than living the life that had been bestowed upon them during the atrocious Battle of Okinawa).

My international travels have included delightful trips to places ranging from the Amazon jungle and Machu Picchu in Peru to living in Negril, Jamaica and visiting islands throughout the Caribbean. I have trekked through a volcanic region in Guatemala. I have also made sure to take in the classic cities of London, Paris, Rome, Madrid and more, and to some of the largest cities in the world including Tokyo and Mexico City.

Final reflections:
Nothing'll stop the US Air Force

Growing up in an uber-patriotic environment on an Air Force base, I became very aware of a strong and unyielding set of restrictions, rules, and military philosophies by which *everyone* must abide. I also was aware that my dad was serving with pride in a branch of the armed forces and, as such, we had to respect and obey certain protocols relative to our behavior. I learned at an early age the lyrics of the official Air Force Song, which set the tone for my dad's line of work and the important role he was playing as an employee of the United States Air Force (USAF). The lyrics of the USAF song, simply titled "US Air Force" (also known as "Wild Blue Yonder") are:

US AIR FORCE (SONG)

"Off we go into the wild blue yonder,
Climbing high into the sun.
Here they come zooming to meet our thunder.
At 'em, boys, give'er the gun! (Give'er the gun now!)

Down we dive, spouting our flame from under
Off with one helluva roar!
We live in fame or go down in flame. Hey!
Nothing'll stop the US Air Force!"

Photo courtesy: Rob Oechsle
US Air Force Aircraft

The powerful lyrics of that anthem express my overall feelings about the influence that growing up in Okinawa and the Air Force life had upon the way I learned to view the world. The words proclaim that "Nothing'll stop the US Air Force." Both in school and at home, we were also taught that if we tried hard, like the US Air Force, "Nothing'll stop us!"

We were encouraged to take those lyrics to heart and apply them to our own lives, especially as we pick up after the impact of the COVID-19 pandemic on all aspects of society. I am in awe of and thankful for the important job that is being and has been done by the soldiers in all the branches of the US Armed Forces stationed in Okinawa. Because of their work, we all can sleep well at night knowing that they are keeping us safe and free.

Photo courtesy: Donn Cuson
Soldiers 1962

As I close this chapter, I want to thank all the current soldiers and veterans of the United States Air Force as the "Aerial Warfare Service" of the US Armed Forces. I greatly appreciate the experience of growing up in the Air Force. We were all made very aware of the important jobs they do to contribute to the USAF mission to:

"Fly, fight and win in air, space and cyberspace."

Now that our tour of Okinawa is completed, in the next chapter, you will learn more about what you can do to achieve healthy aging by practicing eight common Healthy Longevity Principles that people like the Okinawans and others in the "Blue Zones" utilize to live long and enriching lives.

PART II:

WHAT CAN I DO TO LIVE A LONG & HEALTHY LIFE?

Photo courtesy: Rob Oechsle

Part II will examine what you can do to live a long and healthy life. In it, you will learn about:

- MRAF's 8 Healthy Longevity Principles, practiced by people who are successful at healthy aging, and how to apply them to your life.
- How to FINALLY find your IKIGAI (Reason for Being!) AND add seven years to your life.

CHAPTER 5:

MRAF's "8 Healthy Longevity Principles"

A formula for a healthy, happy, and fulfilled life

After researching the quantitative and qualitative work of international experts on how exactly one achieves healthy longevity, I developed a unique model. It sums up current facts and knowledge about what leading experts have identified as the common practices employed by healthy and life-fulfilled people who live the longest.

Let us begin by exploring my model, *MRAF's "8 Healthy Longevity Principles."* (FYI, MRAF are my initials.) This is a recipe for anyone interested in finally achieving a long, healthy, happy, and fulfilled life.

MRAF's
8 Healthy Longevity
Principles

You Are What You Eat & Drink

1. Eat 80% Between Famine & Feast (Hara Hachi Bu)

2. Go Fish, Green, Bean & Lean

Destress from Stress

3. Imbibe & Unwind with Wine @ 5

4. Shake off Stress

5. Get in the Groove & Move

LB2: Love, Be Loved, & Belong

6. Family & Friends First

7. Choose the Community & Company You Keep

Let YOUR Little Light Shine Higher

8. Find YOUR IKIGAI (Reason for Being!) Then, Live YOUR Dreams Daily

© OKI ME LLC, Martha RA Fields

Ingredients for the "Healthy Longevity" Recipe

Prominent researchers have discovered that people who live the longest and are the healthiest use several common ingredients to concoct a lifestyle *and* environment that contributes to their longevity. Based upon information gathered from reputable global experts, I have developed a model to create a healthy aging recipe. It is called "MRAF's 8 Healthy Longevity Principles" and involves practicing these eight principles:

You Are What You Eat and Drink.

1. Eat 80% between famine & feast (Hara Hachi Bu).
2. Go fish, green, bean & lean.

De-stress from Stress.

3. Imbibe & unwind with wine @5.
4. Shake off stress.
5. Get in the groove & move.

LB2: Love. Be Loved. Belong.

6. Family & friends first.
7. Choose the community & company you keep.

Let Your Little Light Shine Higher.

8. Find YOUR IKIGAI (Reason for Being!). Then, live your dreams daily.

What follows is an in-depth explanation of my MRAF's "8 Healthy Longevity Principles" model. Before we begin to stir up this recipe, I would like you to complete this brief Healthy Aging Trivia Quiz. It will test your knowledge about topics covered in this chapter.

Healthy Aging Trivia Quiz

Test your knowledge about healthy aging by completing this quiz!

Directions: Without using any electronic devices, please complete this Healthy Aging Trivia Quiz by circling your answers. At the end, score your responses and see how well you performed.

1. The phrase "eating until you're 80% full" refers to:
A. Eating 80% of the food on your plate
B. Eating only 20% of the food on your plate
C. *Hara hachi bu*: Only eat until you are 80% full/no longer hungry or eat until you are eight parts full (out of ten)

2. After you have eaten something, how long does it take for the "stretch receptors" in your stomach to tell your brain that you are full?
A. 5 minutes
B. 20 minutes
C. 30 minutes

3. What type of a bean is edamame?
A. Soy
B. Fava
C. Green pea

4. When people live to 100 years old, do they typically experience:
A. A rapid terminal decline early in life relative to their health
B. A rapid terminal decline in health late in their lives
C. None of the above

5. Which of these things are good for your health:
A. Dark chocolate
B. Purple sweet potatoes (Beni imo)
C. Goya (Bitter melon)
D. All the above

6. Which fish is full of omega-3 and helps keep you healthy?
A. Salmon

| B. Flounder |
| C. Snapper |
| D. All the above |

7. Can drinking one or two glasses of red wine every day help prolong your life?
A. Yes
B. No
C. It depends

8. This is the beverage that is most highly recommended by experts because of its health benefits:
A. Sardinian Cannonau (a red wine)
B. Sake
C. Vodka
D. Awamori (Okinawan sake)

9. Having a sense of purpose that you get up every morning eager to fulfill can add this number of years to your life:
A. 0 years
B. 7 years
C. 15 years

10. Based on research, these are the major elements that contribute to your ability to live a long and healthy life:
A. Genes and family
B. Lifestyle and environment
C. Exercise and sleep

Healthy Aging Trivia Quiz Answers

See how well you performed on this quiz about healthy aging
by reviewing the answers and scoring instructions below.

1. **C -- Hara Hachi Bu: Only eat until you are 80% full/no longer hungry or eat until you are eight parts full (out of ten)**
2. **B -- 20 minutes**
3. **A -- Soy**
4. **B -- A rapid terminal decline in health late in their lives**
5. **D -- All the above**
6. **D -- All the above**
7. **A -- Yes**
8. **A -- Sardinian Cannonau (A Red Wine)**
9. **B -- 7 years**
10. **B -- Lifestyle and Environment**

HOW TO INTERPRET YOUR SCORE

For each question you got right, give yourself ONE (1) point. Add up all your points and list your total below:

MY TOTAL POINTS: (Insert your number here)_____

If your total points were:

- **Eight (8) to Ten (10) Points**: You are *extremely* enlightened about healthy longevity. Keep up the fabulous work.

- **Four (4) to Seven (7) Points:** You have a *moderate* understanding and can gain from learning more through this book. Keep striving to obtain more knowledge.

- **Zero (0) to Three (3) Points:** You *barely* have a basic understanding of healthy longevity. Great thing you are reading this book to learn more!

How well did you do on the quiz? Do not worry if you did not answer every question correctly. In the following pages, you will gain more in-depth knowledge to help you better understand the answers. Get ready to bake your recipe for healthy aging, as we explore the eight principles practiced in common by people who lead healthy and long lives.

MRAF's "8 Healthy Longevity Principles"
Overview
Proven secrets to successful healthy aging

After weeding through countless research documents, books, articles, and studies, I found that many experts cited some form of these eight principles practiced by those who want to achieve success at life and work by staying healthy while growing older. As we review these eight principles, I will point out what you can do to incorporate them into your life.

Our first category, **You are what you eat and drink,** includes Principle 1 and Principle 2.

Principle 1: Eat 80% Between Famine and Feast by Practicing Hara Hachi Bu.

Image courtesy: Rob Oechsle
Created by: Eliphalet M. Brown, Jr.
1853 hand-colored lithograph, first photo ever taken in Japan at Naha City

Hara hachi bu = Only eat until you are 80% full.

It is said that the concept of *hara hachi bu* dates back some 2,500 years to Confucius. The term's translation is "Eat until you are 80% full." After learning about this doctrine, I discovered that it was in opposition to what I was taught growing up.

Like many kids "back in the day," I was told by my parents that I "must eat all the food on my plate." Everything on it *must* be consumed or I simply could not leave the table until that task was completed. Whenever I complained about being full, I was reminded that I was lucky to have such good food and should "think about the starving children in China" (or sometimes Africa) and "appreciate how fortunate we are in this country."

It is amazing that just about everyone I knew growing up was told similar things. As I reflect on that advice from well-meaning parents, including my own, I see how bad that directive was relative to healthy longevity. For me, it led to years of obesity and overeating.

After returning to Okinawa in 2016 and learning about the concept of hara hachi bu, I realized that the "starving kids in China" probably were taught the healthy longevity concept of eating only until they were 80% full. When food was available, they probably stopped consuming it (as I have now learned to do) when they were no longer hungry.

Why should people stop eating when they are 80% full? Here is a scientific answer to that question. When you eat something, it takes the "stretch receptors" in your stomach about 20 minutes to signal to your brain, through the hormone cholecystokinin, that you are full. This delayed response means that if you continue eating after your hunger has been satisfied, you will be consuming 20% more food than needed at each meal. Eating extra calories expands your stomach every time that occurs, with the result that you then must eat more to feel full and satisfied. This habit causes weight gain and can lead to obesity and chronic health conditions.

On my trip to Okinawa during the Christmas 2016 and New Year's 2017 holiday season, I learned about hara hachi bu. I realized that I should no longer listen to what my mom and dad said about "eating everything on my plate" but to practice this approach.

I finally recognized that I should not eat until I am full (as I had been conditioned), but instead:

Stop eating when I am no longer hungry!

When I first discovered this fabulous concept, people in Okinawa told me that I would know when I was not hungry if I listened to my body. They were right. I came to recognize when I no longer felt hunger pains. Then, like Okinawans, I would put down my knife, fork, spoon, or chopsticks and stop eating.

One small note: while I utter the words "hara hachi bu" at the time when I am no longer hungry, many Okinawan elders, however, utter that phrase *before* they begin to eat. This ritual reminds them to practice the concept while enjoying their food. Why not try this powerful technique? It may help you shed and keep off unwanted pounds that endanger your healthy aging journey.

Who to believe about diet and healthy aging?

While writing this section, I was reminded of a conversation with a friend about new diet trends. She said: "Just as I was giving up butter, experts said it was okay to use it. A few years later, they changed and said it was bad for you. Same thing with red wine. I heard it was the best thing for your health. So, I stopped drinking chardonnay and made red wine my beverage of choice. Then, I read a report saying it is a myth that red wine, even in moderation, is good for you and it is best to abstain from *all* alcohol. I wish they'd make up their minds!"

I cannot argue with my friend about how quickly information changes about healthy eating and drinking. Scientific and medical research does evolve frequently. The top trend today can be tossed in the trash tomorrow with a breaking news story. Having said that, I am sure that some of the healthy longevity practices discussed in this book may change or even become irrelevant over time. The information I have chosen to share, however, is accurate and relevant at the time of my writing.

So, what should one do to stay abreast of accurate advice on healthy aging? While there is no easy solution, I recommend tuning into both trending and traditional discoveries and discussing them with your physician and other healthcare providers to determine what is best for your circumstances.

What should I eat?

To master the concept of hara hachi bu, it is important to understand what to eat for healthy longevity. One approach is to practice the "traditional Okinawan diet." This term is used to connote the manner indigenous Okinawans throughout the ages have eaten. Please note that while there are other healthy diets that can be effective, such as the Mediterranean and keto (ketogenic) diets, I will not be reviewing them in detail in this book.

If you want to obtain an in-depth knowledge about the traditional Okinawan diet, I highly recommend the classic book, *The Okinawan Program*.

It is a huge book at 484 pages and is authored by three esteemed medical and scientific research experts on healthy longevity in Okinawa. They are:

- Okinawan doctor Makoto Suzuki, MD, and
- Two American twin brothers, Bradley J. Willcox, MD, and D. Craig Willcox, PhD.

The book based on their research is packed with pearls of wisdom about healthy aging. Topics range from Eastern and Western approaches to diet and medicine to exercise, supportive social networks, psycho-spiritual influences, and stress reduction. Here is how the authors summarize the incredible impact of the Okinawan diet on healthy aging:

> "…Their diet alone is a powerful prescription for lifelong health. Their low-calorie, plant-based diet high in unrefined carbohydrates… affords protection against most diseases associated with premature aging, including coronary heart

disease, cancer, and stroke, and gives people the best shot at remaining slim and healthy for life. This has been clearly supported by the scientific literature, including our research, and debunks the popular low-carbohydrate diet craze."[37]

These Okinawan food proverbs summarize how much food is revered in their society.

"Eat less in order to live longer."
"Food should nourish life—this is the best medicine."

Research indicates that food has both a positive and negative impact upon healthy aging. It can be excellent medicine for the soul but if abused can lead to chronic disease and terminal illness. Okinawans respect food and take great care when growing it in their gardens or serving it to loved ones whether daily or on a special occasion. How the food is presented is as equally important as how it is prepared.

Overview of the Okinawan diet

✓ If you google "Okinawan diet," you may be overwhelmed by the abundance of articles and research on this topic. The traditional Okinawan diet is low in calories and saturated fats but high in complex carbohydrates. It is mostly plant-based and includes large amounts of vegetables and beans/legumes (especially soy). Okinawans also consume small amounts of fish and meat, which are used as flavorings rather than the main attraction on a plate. While visiting Okinawa, I was surprised to learn that they LOVE pork. One caveat—it is only eaten in moderation or on special celebratory occasions. The secret is in the preparation. Pork is often stewed for long periods and the fat is skimmed off, leaving behind high-protein collagens.

---

[37]   Makoto Suzuki, Bradley J. Willcox, and D. Craig Willcox. *The Okinawa Program: Learn the Secrets to Healthy Longevity* (New York: Three Rivers Press, 2001), 6.

✓ My biggest "aha" about the Okinawan diet is that unlike in many Asian cultures, white rice is not a significant part of their cuisine. While they do consume some white and brown rice, their main staple is a purple sweet potato called *beni imo*. About 60% of the Okinawan diet before 1940 consisted of beni imo. *Goyain/goya* is another popular food. This is a bitter melon that resembles a long, pimply cucumber but has a strong bitter taste that you may need to acquire. More about these wonder foods shortly.

Okinawans tend not to eat grains and eat few or no processed foods, sugar, or refined sweets. Dairy products are not consumed or only used occasionally. Many foods eaten possess high levels of antioxidants that may reduce the risk of chronic illnesses, some cancers and cardiovascular disease.

Medical expert Michael Greger, MD, offers this advice:

> "From a nutrition standpoint, I would much rather see people eat, for example, the traditional Okinawan diet, which is largely (but not exclusively) plant-based, than the strictest 100% vegan diet centered around French fries and vegan doughnuts. Unprocessed plain foods are the healthiest options; so, the more we can squeeze into our daily diet the better. Health-wise it doesn't really matter what we eat on holidays or special occasions; it's our week-to-week choices that make the most difference for our long-term health and longevity."[38]

Fast food's negative impact on Okinawan diet

Unfortunately, younger Okinawans today are not always following in the healthy dietary footsteps of their older citizens. When I visit Okinawa, I am always startled by the massive number of fast-food establishments. McDonald's, KFC, A&W Restaurants, Domino's Pizza, and more are all alive and well in the world's healthy longevity capitol.

---

[38] "How Not to Die: 9 Questions for Dr. Michael Greger," Blue Zones, https://www.bluezones.com/2015/12/how-not-to-die-9-questions-for-michael-greger-md/. Accessed May 4, 2018.

Photo by: MRAF
McDonald's in Okinawa

The trend of younger Okinawans deviating from their ancestors' traditional diet as well as the lure of fast-food restaurants is starting a devastating trend relative to life expectancy in Okinawa. There are signs that life expectancy rates are starting to decline. The consumption of fast foods is also increasing the waistlines of some Okinawans and more cases of obesity are being reported.

What is the typical traditional Okinawan diet?

According to the *Okinawa Program* authors, traditional Okinawan elders on average eat these things daily:

- "Seven servings of vegetables and fruits
- Seven servings of grains
- Two servings of flavonoid-rich soy products
- Omega-3-rich fish (at least three times a week)
- Minimal dairy products and meat."[39]

---

[39]   Suzuki et al., *The Okinawa Program*, (2001), 69.

Author Sally Beare adds these insights about Okinawans and food:

> "The Okinawans have a saying, *Ishoku-dogen*, meaning, literally, 'food and medicine from the same source.' Their food is rich in anticancer, antiaging antioxidants—the miracle molecules that neutralize age-promoting free radicals... Okinawan food is unique to Japan in that it is influenced by both Chinese and Japanese cooking with its pork and vegetable dishes from China as well as fish and seaweed dishes from Japan, the diet contains a wide range of nutrients."[40]

Photo by: MRAF

More popular Okinawan foods

Here are some additional foods contained in the traditional Okinawan diet:

- ✓ Herbs and spices, especially ginger, garlic, mugwort, and especially turmeric.
- ✓ Turmeric is a "wonder spice" with amazing medical properties. The sporamin in turmeric has antiaging properties. Researchers have found that the compound curcumin in it slows the progression of dementia.
- ✓ Seaweed, especially kombu (an edible kelp) and wakame. They are popular ingredients in soups and stews.

---

[40] Sally Beare, *50 Secrets of the World's Longest Living People* (Cambridge, MA: Da Capo Press, 2006), 1.

✓ Shitake mushrooms
✓ Hechima, **a widely-consumed vegetable that some say tastes like a sweet zucchini.**
✓ Soybeans and soy products including tofu
✓ Miso is a traditional seasoning that is created by fermenting soybeans with other grains (such as rice or barley) and mixed with salt and the fungus *koji* (Aspergillus oryzae)
✓ Miso soup is made from a miso paste. The green leaves from sweet potatoes are often an ingredient in the popular miso soup.

Typical Okinawan Beverages

Popular beverages for Okinawans include:

✓ Water
✓ Jasmine tea
✓ Turmeric tea
✓ Mugwort tea
✓ Matcha tea
✓ Awamori, a sake (alcoholic beverage) that is indigenous to Okinawa and made from long-grain indica rice. It is aged in traditional pots that increase and improve its flavor.
✓ Beer. Orion is one of the most popular beers consumed in Okinawa. Sapporo is the oldest beer brand in Japan, founded in 1876.

Okinawan superfoods you may not know but should try

There are two Okinawan superfoods that you may not know about but should try. I have discovered them on my trips to Okinawa. Why should you take the plunge and try them? Not only are they extremely good for you, but the people who live the longest and healthiest swear by them and include them as main staples of their healthy longevity diet. These foods include:

- ***Beni imo (purple sweet potatoes)***
- ***Goya (a bitter melon)***

Beni imo, or purple sweet potatoes

WHAT IS THE #1 HEALTH FOOD IN THE OKINAWAN DIET?

It is the Japanese purple sweet potato (beni imo)

Have you noticed more sweet potato products at the supermarket lately? More grocery stores and restaurants are carrying things like sweet potato fries, chips, and pies. This is no coincidence, because sweet potatoes are extremely healthy for you and can promote healthy aging.

Purple sweet potatoes are a staple in the traditional Okinawan diet. The Japanese word for purple is "beni" and sweet potato is "imo."

Beni imo is a superfood that has many wonderful characteristics, including being extraordinarily high in vitamin C, fiber, and beta-carotene, which researchers have identified as having cancer-fighting properties. It is rich in fiber, vitamin A (one potato has four times the recommended daily dose) and vitamin C. Beni imo is used in multiple ways, as part of stir-fries, and in ice cream, breads, cakes, and other pastries like purple brownies and cheesecake. I particularly like the mega-popular Blue Seal Ice Cream's beni imo-flavor ice cream. The beni imo tart is a popular treat and is filled with piped purple cream swirls in a small boat-like tart. During and after austere times following WWII, the purple sweet potato kept many people alive.

Photo by: MRAF
Goya/Goyain, another "must try" Okinawan superfood

Okinawans also frequently partake of a prickly cucumber-like bitter melon called "goyain" or "goya." Some say it looks like a differently-formed cucumber with pimply green skin. If you are not familiar with it, you should put it on your shopping list and try it. (The name of this bitter melon, however, should not be confused with the popular Spanish food line Goya.)

It is also rich in beta-carotene, which makes for a natural energy booster. In addition, it has been shown to improve the immune system and reduce the incidence of flu and colds. People use it to relieve constipation, balance blood sugar levels, detox the liver and assist in food digestion.

Because Okinawan goya is so bitter, one may need to acquire a taste for it. Goya is often served in a popular stir-fry concoction called "champuru." Goya champuru typically contains the bitter goya melon along with canola oil, tofu, eggs, and black pepper. Some disguise the bitter taste by adding curry, green chili peppers, tomatoes, onion, and garlic.

While this bitter melon is not widely used in the United States, it has been used for generations by shamans in China, North America, Africa, and India. It has incredible nutritional value and healing properties. It contains huge amounts of vitamin C, magnesium, fiber, phosphorus, manganese, zinc, and vitamins B1, B2, and B3. It has about double the amount of potassium as bananas and two times more calcium than spinach.

Superpowers of goya

According to the authors of *The Okinawa Program*, the "Chinese and Okinawans have used the fruit, seeds, vines, stems and leaves for gastrointestinal maladies, including chronic stomach ulcers and dysentery. Other uses include the treatment of fever, viral infections, and toothaches. Chronic diseases such as diabetes, cancer, rheumatism, gout, and spleen and liver disorders have also been treated with goya. It has even been claimed to act as a male aphrodisiac."[41]

Where to find beni imo and goya

You might find beni imo or goya in your local Asian, Chinese, Japanese, and East Indian markets. I have had luck finding these where I work in Boston at stores in our downtown Chinatown community and at a chain of Asian supermarkets called Super 88.

High in complex carbohydrates

The fact that the Okinawan diet is high in complex carbohydrates may come as a surprise, especially since complex carbohydrates are found in pasta, white flour, bread, and other low-nutrition foods generally regarded as "unhealthy." Some complex carbohydrates, however, can provide important fiber, minerals, and vitamins. It should be noted that Okinawans consume certain types of complex carbohydrates as those found in vegetables.

The key to maintaining a healthy digestive system is fiber. Fiber is a complex carbohydrate derived from plant-based foods. Fiber is composed of sugar molecules that are strung together in long and complex chains. An article in *Medical News Today* explains the importance of complex carbohydrates:

> "Complex carbohydrates contain longer chains of sugar molecules than simple carbohydrates. The body converts these sugar molecules into glucose, which it uses for energy. As complex carbohydrates have longer chains, they take

---

[41]   Suzuki et al., *The Okinawa Program*, (2001), 153.

longer to break down and provide more lasting energy in the body than simple carbohydrates."[42]

Complex carbohydrates that should be included in a healthy aging diet include:

- Legumes/peas and beans
- Nuts
- Vegetables
- Whole grains: oats, barley, brown rice, and buckwheat

No or few refined carbohydrates

The Okinawan diet contains no or few refined carbohydrates. These are carbohydrates which do not naturally occur in nature and exist because of human processing. (The processing removes fiber and a lot of nutritional value.) Refined carbohydrates can be highly addictive and include:

- Sugar
- Grains: white and "quick-cook" rice, corn, wheat
- Potatoes
- Enriched and bleached flours
- Fruit juice concentrates
- Breakfast cereals
- White pasta
- White and sourdough breads, bagels, pizza, and biscuits
- Processed meats: sausage, hot dogs, and cold cuts
- Soft drinks
- Snack foods (empty foods/little nutritional value): cookies, cakes, candy, potato and corn chips, and pies

My firsthand observation is that Okinawans tend to eat a lot of different food types in a meal. Their success lies in *what* they eat. Principle 2 provides more information on what healthy and long-lived people typically eat.

---

[42] Aaron Kandola; medically reviewed by Katherine Marengo. *"What to Know About Simple and Complex Carbs?" Medical News Today.* May 14, 2019.

This is an example of a meal with lots of food variety that I was served in a traditional Okinawan restaurant in Chatan.

Photo by: MRAF
A traditional Okinawan meal. Lots of variety and small portions.

Principle 2: Go Fish, Green, Bean, and Lean.

The second of MRAF's "8 Healthy Longevity Principles" is: Go fish, green, bean, and lean.

Photo By: MRAF
Sunglass fish in Naha, Okinawa

Hot Tip: I took this picture in an Okinawan market. The sunglasses-wearing fish is a reminder to eat fish rich in omega-3 fatty acids *and* get plenty of vitamin D from the sun.

Omega-3-rich fish

Many people who live long and healthy lives include in their diet omega-3-rich fish that has been caught in the wild with low mercury—avoid anything genetically farmed. Such fish and seafood include:

- _____Anchovies
- _____Atlantic mackerel
- _____Black sea bass
- _____Bonito
- _____Catfish
- _____Clams
- _____Cod
- _____Crabs
- _____Crawfish
- _____Eel (unagi or anago)
- _____Flounder
- _____Grouper
- _____Haddock
- _____Halibut
- _____Herring
- _____Horse mackerel
- _____Lobster
- _____Pacific saury
- _____Salmon
- _____Sardines
- _____Scallops
- _____Sea bream
- _____Shrimp
- _____Skate
- _____Snapper
- _____Sole
- _____Squid
- _____Tilapia
- _____Trout
- _____Tuna (canned, light)
- _____Yellowtail

Add more fish to your diet by visiting your local fishmonger, grocer, or favorite fishing spot. Okinawans prefer cold-water fish high in omega-3 fatty acids, such as tuna and salmon.

Should you eat meat?

Meat can be consumed in a healthy longevity diet, but only in moderation or on special occasions and in small amounts. One palm-size piece (or about three ounces) is the equivalent of one portion. If you eat meat, experts stress that free-range and organic-fed choices are the best. As noted above, to my surprise, Okinawans *love* pork. They consume just about every inch of the pig. While things like pig feet, tongue, intestines, and other innards were not something I fancied, I decided that if Okinawans live to be 110+ then I should try what they are having and experiment with some items that my palate would not normally experience. In Okinawa, I did partake of pig innards soup and pig ears. Both were not bad, but honestly, I cannot ever see myself craving those items.

I mentioned to a restaurant owner and friend named Takuya Nakahashi, who is Japanese and owns several successful restaurants in Okinawa, that where I live in the USA people are told to avoid eating pork. He proceeded to provide me with an enriching agricultural lesson. He explained that perhaps people in Okinawa are healthy yet eat certain meats like pork and beef is because of how the farmers raise these animals. He noted that livestock are often fed only organic products like grass and are not pumped up with chemicals and preservatives. He also felt that the clean environment in Okinawa might also contribute to healthier pork and beef.

Photo by: MRAF
Super 88 Market in Malden, Massachusetts

Okinawans LOVE pork and eat just about every part of the pig, but in moderation only!

Here is what Dan Buettner had to say about Okinawans' consumption of pork:

"I visited Dr. Kazuhiko Taira, an MD and faculty member in the Department of Tourism Sciences at University of the Ryukyus. For 20 years…he updated his survey of centenarians in Okinawa and found that Okinawans suffer significantly fewer strokes. He believed that it was related to diet, specifically the eating of less salt and more pork…A salt-heavy diet may contribute to high blood pressure and weakened arteries, he said, causing micro-tears that are precursors to strokes. Consuming a balance of both animal and plant protein through pork may help repair or retard those tears…'Okinawa people eat most every part of the pig,' Taira said. There is a lot of vitamin B and B2 in it, and collagen, which is good for you…Too much animal protein can increase your chances of obesity; the Okinawan centenarians traditionally ate meat only during infrequent ceremonial occasions."[43]

One final note on eating pork. How Okinawans cook pork may account for why they can still eat it and remain healthy. Often, pork dishes are boiled or stewed for long hours. The fat is skimmed off in the cooking process so what is finally eaten has significantly lower amounts of fat. What a great way to have your pork, eat it, too, *and* live a long and healthy life!

Plant-based meats

Plant-based meats have become a huge trend. While plant-based meats involve different ingredients, they may include extracted soy, wheat, whey, or pea protein. According to Unilever Food Solutions, here are some advantages of eating plant-based meats:

"Plant-based protein is tied to a number of positives for people and the planet. Swapping meat for plants reduces saturated fat and increases the fiber and vitamin content of dishes. Studies show that this leads to reduced risks for

---

[43] Dan Buettner, *The Blue Zones: Second Edition. 9 Lessons for Living Longer from the people who've lived the longest.* (Washington, DC: National Geographic Society, 2012), 76-77.

diabetes, cancer, and heart disease. Also, plants require fewer environmental resources like water and space, which can offset climate change. Finally, vegetarian proteins are food sources that animal lovers can feel good about eating."[44]

KFC (formerly known as Kentucky Fried Chicken) has introduced the "Beyond Fried Chicken," a plant-based "chicken" nugget. This is the first plant-based protein to be sold at a national US-based fast-food chicken chain and was created exclusively for KFC by the Beyond Meat Company. The "Beyond Burger" plant-based hamburger brand has been flying off grocery shelves.

The Beyond Meat website states that its mission is as follows: "At Beyond Meat, we believe there is a better way to feed the planet. Our mission is to create The Future of Protein-- delicious plant-based burgers, beef, sausage, crumbles and more. By shifting from animal to plant-based meat, we can address four growing global issues: human health, climate change, constraints on natural resources and animal welfare."[45]

Burger King, the second-largest hamburger chain in the US, in August 2019 began selling, with great fanfare, their plant-based hamburger called the Impossible Whopper. When it first came on the market, I felt like every other commercial on TV was about this new phenomenon.

I will admit that the intense advertising piqued my curiosity about whether they could produce a burger from a plant that tasted like a *real* hamburger. I decided to take a plunge and try one. In all honesty, I was prepared to not like it. While waiting in line for my order, I picked up a flyer that had a picture on front with the caption, "IMPOSSIBLE WHOPPER. 100% WHOPPER. 0% BEEF."

---

44 Unilever Foods Solutions, "The Future of Meat: The Rise in Plant Based Alternatives." https://www.unileverfoodsolutions.ca/en/chef-inspiration/plant-based-eating/trends/meat-alternatives.html. Accessed February 8, 2020.

45 Beyond Meat, "Our Mission," https://www.beyondmeat.com/about/. Accessed 02-08-2020.

The information on the back of this flyer said the main ingredients in the patty are "soy and potato protein, coconut oil, and sunflower oil." I could not finish reading the entire promo before they called my number to pick up my order. After sitting down in a booth, I unwrapped the burger and extensively investigated to determine if it *really* looked like a hamburger. It passed the test. Closing the bun, I took a bite, and, to my utter surprise, it was delicious. I could *not* tell the difference between the plant-based imposter and the real thing!

Words of caution about plant-based meats

While chomping on my burger, I finally finished read the Burger King flyer. I was taken aback by a statement that commented on how it is cooked: **"HOW IS IT COOKED?** The IMPOSSIBLE patty is 0% beef. It is made entirely from plant-based sources, but it is cooked on the same broiler as our WHOPPER patties. Let the restaurants know if you would like your IMPOSSIBLE patty prepared without using the broiler!"[46]

I thought it strange that the company had gone to great lengths to produce a plant-based product but would cook it on a broiler where animal hamburger meat was also prepared. If you are a vegetarian, it is important to be aware of this dynamic.

Another caution. One would think that a plant-based burger would be lower in calories. To my amazement, I found that this is not always the case. The number of calories contained in plant-based meats is often the same or close to their animal meat counterparts. For example, the animal meat version of the Whopper has 660 calories (more than half of them from 40 grams of fat and 28 grams of protein.) The plant-based Impossible Whopper has 630 calories (half from 34 grams of fat and 25 grams of protein.)

---

[46]   Source: Burger King Corporation. Impossible is a trademark of Impossible Foods Inc.

Photo by: MRAF

"Go Green"

The second component of Principle 2 is "Go green." Healthy aging diets are full of green leafy vegetables. They are cholesterol-free, low in calories and sodium, full of vitamins C and A, plus fiber, calcium, folate, and phytonutrients. If you are interested in "greening up your diet," choose seasonal and locally sold and grown foods, including the following fantastic dark green leafy vegetables:

- _____Beet greens
- _____Broccoli
- _____Chard
- _____Collard greens
- _____Dandelion
- _____Kale
- _____Mustard greens
- _____Purslane
- _____Spinach

"Go bean"

Our next ingredient in the Principle 2 recipe for a healthy longevity diet is to "go bean" by consuming beans (legumes), which are an excellent addition to any healthy aging diet. Legume-rich diets are often associated with less colon cancer and fewer heart attacks because they are a fantastic source of fiber and healthy flavonoids. Almost any type of bean is good for you, but soybeans are especially healthy. Do not forget to try some tofu, the main ingredient of which is soy. The Spanish food company, Goya, has a product called sixteen-bean soup that I particularly like. Yes, it does contain sixteen different beans.

Some beans/legumes you may want to partake of include:

- _____Black beans and peas
- _____Broad beans
- _____Butter beans
- _____Chickpeas
- _____Fava beans
- _____Kidney beans
- _____Lentils
- _____Lima beans
- _____Navy beans
- _____Pinto beans
- _____Soybeans/tofu/edamame
- _____Split peas

Great protein sources

Eating soy-rich foods can add protein to your diet. Peas, beans, and whole grains are other good sources. Nuts are great as a snack or mixed into dishes. They are generally a good source of protein and fiber. Here is a list of nuts that are healthy and scrumptious items to place on your healthy longevity diet grocery list:

- _____Almonds
- _____Brazil nuts
- _____Cashews
- _____Hazelnuts
- _____Peanuts (Note: They are technically a legume, not a nut)
- _____Pistachios
- _____Pumpkin seeds
- _____Soy nuts
- _____Sunflower seeds
- _____Walnuts

Gourds and other vegetables

These gourd vegetables should also be added to your healthy aging diet:

- _____ Beni imo (purple sweet potato)
- _____ Goya (bitter melon)

- _____ Hechima (sponge gourd)
- _____ Pumpkin
- _____ Red sweet potato
- _____ Squash
- _____ Summer squash
- _____ Wax gourd

Antioxidants and aging

Numerous studies have examined the impact of antioxidants on aging. Antioxidants are

> "…substances that keep you young and healthy by increasing immune function, decreasing the risk of infection and cancer, and, most important, by protecting against free-radical damage. Free radicals are cellular desperados that play a pivotal role in the aging process, and their damage takes a toll on virtually every organ in the aging human body. This in turn sets the stage for all sorts of degenerative diseases, including Alzheimer's and other forms of dementia. Antioxidants neutralize free radicals and keep them in place…*If your diet is high in antioxidants, your risk of many age – associated diseases – including cancer, heart disease, macular degeneration, and cataracts – decreases*…Many studies published in the world's most prestigious medical journals have demonstrated the benefits of diets high in antioxidants in preventing Alzheimer's and other forms of dementia and cognitive decline."[47]

Fantastic antioxidants are contained in vitamins C, D, and E. Minerals like zinc and magnesium are also antioxidants. Some fresh fruits, beans/legumes, vegetables, and whole grains also contain antioxidants.

---

[47]   John Robbins, *Healthy at 100: How You Can-at any age-Dramatically Increase Your Life Span and Your Health Span* (New York: Ballantine Books, 2007), 195.

"Bad" foods that are good for you

Check out the items below that you may have thought were "bad" but are good for you. Remember that the key is to add them to your diet *in moderation.*

Chocolate

For centuries, people worldwide have savored the taste of chocolate. Did you know that eating dark chocolate can contribute to healthy aging? Studies have shown that dark chocolate has multiple health benefits. It lowers the risk of heart disease, stabilizes blood sugar, and reduces cravings that could lead to weight gain.

Dark chocolate is made from the seeds of the cacao tree and contains these healthy aging elements:

- Fiber
- Copper
- Iron
- Phosphorus
- Potassium
- Zinc

There are, however, some caveats to procuring healthy longevity bonus points from eating dark chocolate.

- Not all chocolate is created equal. To achieve longevity benefits, consume dark chocolate, a much better choice than milk chocolate.
- Dark chocolate is a blend of at least 70%-85% cacao. Check to see that what you eat contains at least those percentages. Select chocolate that is organic and/or fair trade.
- Studies have shown that chocolate organic compounds function as antioxidants. These include polyphenols, flavonoids and catechins, to name a few. These substances have been found to prevent risk factors for heart disease and diabetes.

- Watch the amount of dark chocolate you eat, as it is high in calories and saturated fat. Eat in moderation and indulge in no more than one ounce per day. Overindulging can lead to weight gain, which can negatively impact your overall health and well-being.
- Chocolate can lead to unwanted symptoms such as headaches, heartburn, and indigestion. It can also impact blood pressure, heart rate and moods.
- Phenylethylamine in this savory treat could result in a rapid heartbeat. The cocoa butter contains stimulants like caffeine and theobromine, which could be problematic for people with hypertension and heart disease.
- Mild psychoactive effects can also be produced by consuming chocolate. This includes a feeling of happiness, elation and alertness followed by depression and lethargy. Individuals with diabetes should know that dark chocolate might also cause serious swings in blood sugar levels.

Photo by: MRAF

Dark chocolate: a tasty treat that is good for you.

Spice up your life

Spice up your life and your healthy longevity diet by using these powerful herbs and spices more often:

- _____Chamomile
- _____Cilantro
- _____Cumin
- _____Dill
- _____Fennel
- _____Ginger
- _____Garlic
- _____Marjoram
- _____Mint
- _____Mugwort

- _____Parsley
- _____Rosemary
- _____Sage
- _____Shichimi (a seven-spice powder that includes chili pepper, dried orange peel, hemp seeds, nori seaweed flakes, sansho leaf, white poppy seeds, and white sesame seeds)
- _____Turmeric

Heard a lot about turmeric lately?

Have you noticed that news sources and health gurus have been talking a lot about turmeric lately? There is a reason why this superfood that contains the chemical curcumin has been getting such attention. Turmeric is commonly used in Asia and is an extremely versatile spice that is a cousin to ginger. It is frequently a flavoring in things like curry dishes, cheese, mustard, and butter. It also adds color to certain cosmetics, perfumes, and foods.

What you may not know is how beneficial turmeric can be in combating certain illnesses. If you are not using turmeric in your diet, check out these conditions for which turmeric is used:

- Arthritis
- Heartburn
- Joint pain
- Stomach pain
- Crohn's disease
- Ulcerative colitis
- Diarrhea
- Intestinal gas

- Stomach bloating
- Loss of appetite
- Jaundice
- Liver problems
- Helicobacter pylori (H.pylori)
- Infection
- Stomach Ulcers
- Irritable bowel syndrome (IBS)

- Gallbladder disorders
- High Cholesterol
- A skin condition called lichen planus
- Skin inflammation from radiation
- Fatigue
- Headaches
- Bronchitis
- Colds
- Lung infections
- Hay fever
- Fibromyalgia
- Leprosy
- Fever
- Menstrual problems
- Itchy skin
- Recovery after surgery
- Cancer
- Depression
- Water retention
- Worms
- An autoimmune disease called systemic lupus erythematosus (SLE)
- Tuberculosis
- Urinary bladder inflammation
- Kidney problems
- Apply to the skin for pain relief
- Ringworms
- Sprains
- Swelling
- Bruising
- Leech bites
- Eye infections
- Acne
- Inflammatory skin conditions
- Skin sores
- Soreness inside mouth
- Infected wounds
- Gum disease
- Enema for inflammatory bowel disease

When I discovered *all* the medicinal benefits of turmeric, I immediately purchased some and have been experimenting with it in new dishes. I highly recommend you add it to your spice rack.

Be Lean

"Be lean" is the last component of Principle 2. To stay lean, practice these tips:

- Maintain a low-calorie intake.
- Do not overeat or binge-eat. Moderation in drinking and eating is key. Remember to practice hara hachi bu (eat only until 80% full).

Importance of a low-calorie, nutrient-rich diet

Being lean is also about keeping your weight within a healthy range as well as watching your daily consumption of calories. Appropriate caloric intake varies based upon variables like age, height, weight, level of activity and exercise. In the USA, the average woman consumes about 2000 calories a day to maintain her weight and must cut that to 1500 calories per day to lose up to a pound per week. Males consume 2,500 calories per day and to achieve weight loss, must cut that to 2000 calories per day.

Estimates are that Okinawans consume only about 1,200 calories a day but remember that the Okinawan diet is nutrient-rich. It should be noted that societies where people live long, and healthy lives have a lower daily caloric intake.

The late Roy Wallford, MD, was internationally recognized as a top expert in gerontology. Here were his timeless and powerful insights on the importance of maintaining a low-calorie diet.

There is "… hard, well-controlled and steadfastly confirmed experimental evidence that a low-calorie diet that provides optimum nutrition will greatly:

- Extend average and maximum lifespans
- Postpone the onset and decrease the frequencies of most or all the 'diseases of aging'
- Maintain biomarkers at levels younger than chronological age
- Maintain sexual potency and general vitality
- Maintain ability to engage in sports into advanced age
- Delay deterioration of the brain."[48]

Healthy Aging Dietary Tips

Use these Healthy Aging Dietary Tips to help you use food as medicine. They are presented in three categories:

1. <u>Daily Dosages:</u> Things you should consume every day.

---

[48]   Robbins, *Healthy at 100* (2007), 81-82.

2. <u>Moderation:</u> It is okay to partake of these items but do so sparingly and in moderation.

3. <u>Evil so Eliminate:</u> Items in this category do evil things to your body and healthy longevity. They should be eliminated.

Daily Dosages

- Put plenty of plants on your daily menu. "Plenty" means that about 95 to 100 percent of your diet is plant-based. I know that is a lot and quite honestly, I am not there yet, either.
- Add variety to your plant-based diet with fruits, seeds, and nuts.
- Go for the leafy dark green vegetables and stay clear of starchy ones. When you fix a plate, it should consist of two-thirds vegetables and one-third or less of meat or fish.
- Let legumes/beans enter your mouth frequently. Consume at least a half-cup to a cup daily.
- Go nuts with nuts. They are high in protein and will keep you energized, and your belly satisfied. Scoop up one or two fistfuls of them per day.
- Wet your mouth with water and lots of it. Try to consume at least eight 6-ounce glasses a day. Do not worry about overdoing it. It is extremely rare for one to overdose on water!
- Consider incorporating tofu or other soybean products into your diet. I know, you may think tofu is boring and has no great taste. Did you know it can absorb the flavor of what you cook it with? Boost your soy intake by changing from white to soy flour.
- Try switching from cow's milk to soymilk. Consider goat or sheep milk. FYI, goat milk can also be eaten as cheese or yogurt.
- Add spice to your food and life by being adventurous and using some of the herbs and spices mentioned previously. Start with the wonder spice, turmeric. Throw in a variety of other herbs and spices like ginger, basil, and garlic to add flavor and years to your life.
- Live it up. Why not try some of the superfoods you learned about in this section? Think about it, if there are more people in Okinawa who live to age 110+ per square feet than anywhere else in the world, why not try eating what they eat? Duh?

- Experiment. What have you got to lose? Try something like purple sweet potatoes, which is the staple of the Okinawan diet. If you cannot find a store that sells these, eat some orange sweet potatoes as a substitute. They not only taste good but can help you become a healthy and happy supercentenarian!

Moderation

- Eat meat in moderation. If you must consume it, eat servings of just three ounces, about the size of a deck of cards. Do not make it the main attraction on your plate. That role is reserved for vegetables. Consider only eating meat on special occasions or in bite-sized portions as a flavoring in dishes.
- Swim away from too much fish. While fish in moderation is safe, do not overindulge. Three ounces of fish (the size of a deck of cards) three times a week is enough.
- Fish not exposed to toxic chemicals, like PCBs or mercury, are best for you. Even small fish like anchovies and sardines can satisfy this requirement.
- Lose your enthusiasm for eggs. Try to eat only about three per week.

Evil, So Eliminate

- Cut down on sugar or eliminate it as much as possible. Losing those empty calories from cakes, cookies, and candies, all of which contain sugar, can help improve your weight and your ability to live a long and healthy life.
- Be done with the white and sourdough bread. If you must partake of that carb, eat a bread made with whole grains.
- Cut down on or eliminate dairy.
- Stop using the salt so freely. The sodium does not help with your heart health. Instead, spice up your life with herbs and spices which add flavor to your meals, not high blood pressure to your body.
- Take processed meats such as sausage and cold cuts off your grocery list. They help you dig an early grave.

- Eliminate soda and carbonated drinks. Why not explore using a variety of teas that Okinawan people drink and see if that sufficiently satisfies your thirst in a healthy way? Consider teas like jasmine and turmeric.

More tips on what to eat and drink to live a long and healthy life

Photo by MRAF
Eat five-color meals

One way to add both healthy nutrition and color to your dinner is to prepare foods that are comprised of five colors: red, yellow, green, white, and black. Some say that the origins of this practice are from a philosophy in Japan inspired by the *shojin ryori*, the rituals of preparing and eating vegetarian Buddhist food.

Here are examples of food types within each color group:

- **Yellow:** Corn and summer squash
- **Green:** Green beans, Brussels sprouts, spinach, collards, celery, and broccoli
- **Red:** Red onions, beets, radicchio, and red cabbage

- **Black:** Black peppercorns, black beans, and black olives
- **White:** Vidalia onions, tofu, mushrooms, cauliflower, and ramen noodles

Eat the rainbow

A magazine called *Okinawa Living* that is produced by the US Marine Corps offered another take on eating a variety of colors. They called it, "Eat the Rainbow!" In their March 2018 issue, they stated: "Everyone has probably heard, 'eat your greens!' But what about reds, oranges, yellows, purples, and blues? Eating a variety of fruits and vegetables is vital because (depending on plant family and color) they differ in nutrients. That is why that old phrase is being tossed out for a newer, better, 'eat the rainbow!'"[49]

To stay healthy, follow these easy Okinawan-inspired tips

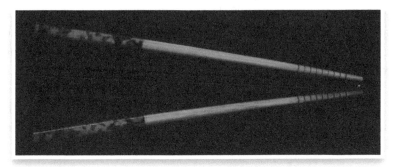

Photo by: Rob Oechsle
Chopsticks

Eat small, bite-sized portions

Using chopsticks to eat food is a good way to keep the portion sizes of foods you consume small. Only a limited amount of food can be placed on a chopstick. Another suggestion is to use smaller plates, which forces you to eat less.

---

[49] Marine Corps Community Service, "Eat the Rainbow!" *Okinawa Living,* Issue 241, March 2018, https://issuu.com/mccsokinawa/docs/march_ol_2018-s53.

Practice conscious eating

The best approach to eating for healthy longevity is to take time to be conscious and conscientious about preparing and eating your food. Conscious eating recognizes that food should be respected and presented in a creative and aesthetic manner. The concept also suggests that one must focus on the food and the joy of eating it, either on your own or with family and friends in a joyous environment.

Eat slowly so your food can be properly chewed and easier to digest. Proper digestion allows you to receive more nutritional value from foods. Focus and become totally absorbed in the pleasant act of eating and do not get distracted from that process by watching TV or utilizing electronic devices.

The Seventh-day Adventist diet

The diet of the Seventh-day Adventists, which is mostly vegetarian or vegan, is cited as an example of a longevity diet that produces healthy aging results. Experts have found that Seventh-day Adventists in Loma Linda, California, live about ten years longer than others in America. Seventh-day Adventists are vegetarians and follow tenets outlined in the Bible. This includes citations from Leviticus 11 and Deuteronomy 4. Leviticus 11 and 13 provide examples of "clean" mammals (cows and chickens) and fish (but only those with fins and scales). Birds that are scavengers (eagles, vultures, and hawks) are not to be eaten.

The Mediterranean diet

Another healthy longevity diet is the "Mediterranean diet" based on the eating patterns of people living in places bordering the Mediterranean Sea, like Italy and Greece. The diet has numerous health benefits including lowering blood pressure, and fighting cancer, heart disease and dementia. The diet is high in fish, vegetables and plant-based foods, whole grains, avocados, fruits, beans, nuts, olive oil and seeds. It also contains moderate amounts of poultry, seafood, dairy, and eggs. Items which are avoided include refined grains (white pasta and bread) and refined oils like soybean and canola oil. Foods with added sugars are also off-limits, including sodas, candies, cakes, and pastries. You may recall that two Blue Zones, Ikaria (Icaria), Greece, and Sardinia, Italy, are in the Mediterranean. Researchers have found that the diets of both places, along with plenty of natural exercise from gardening and walking up and down the mountainous terrain of these spots, have led to healthy longevity in the people of those regions.

You may recall from MRAF's "8 Healthy Longevity Principles" that one of the best red wines for your health is cultivated in Sardinia and called Sardinian Cannonau. I have noticed more wine stores in the USA that carry the delightful vino. Many health experts agree that red wine in moderation (about 1-2 glasses per day) to "downshift" at the end of the day with family and friends is also recommended.

Health benefits of fish

Both the Mediterranean diet and the Okinawan diet include fish. A Harvard doctor shared the positive benefits of eating fish to improve memory. He said:

> "Cognition is a shorthand way of saying thinking, memory, language, attention, visuospatial, and other mental abilities…Fish helps you think — and keeps your thinking strong. What did the researchers find? Fish was the single most important dietary factor in lowering the risk of cognitive impairment. Vegetables were second best, and all other foods showed smaller, insignificant effects.
>
> The take-home lesson: To reduce your risk of cognitive impairment and decline, eat a Mediterranean-style diet including fish several times per week…Just be careful about fish that may have high levels of mercury, such as swordfish and bigeye tuna; these fish should only be eaten occasionally."[50]

---

[50] Andrew E. Budson, "What to Eat to Reduce Your Risk of Alzheimer's Disease." Harvard Health Blog, May 8, 2020. https://www.health.harvard.edu/blog/what-to-eat-to-reduce-your-risk-of-alzheimers-disease-2020050819774.

De-stress from Stress

The next category of the MRAF's "8 Healthy Longevity Principles is to "De-stress from stress." It includes Principles 3, 4 and 5, which are:

- Imbibe and unwind with wine @5.
- Shake off stress.
- Get in the groove and move.

Before writing this chapter, I headed to a trusted dictionary source, Merriam-Webster, to examine the definition of stress. I discovered that it is: "A state of mental or emotional strain or tension resulting from adverse or very demanding circumstances…a physical, chemical or mental tension resulting from factors that tend to alter an existent equilibrium…hormones release throughout the body in response to emotional stress. Synonyms: strain, pressure (nervous) tension, worry, anxiety, trouble, difficulty, and hassle."

Stress may be triggered by positive and negative aspects of life; how each of us responds to stressors differs greatly. A positive life situation, such as a wedding or graduation, is cause for celebration, but for some even a happy event is a mega-stressful situation. When faced with difficult decisions and timelines, some people are motivated and inspired to rise to the occasion while others become overwhelmed. Below are MRAF's three Principles to help you to "Destress from stress."

Principle 3: Imbibe and Unwind with Wine @ 5

The third principle practiced by people who live the longest and are the healthiest is what I call "imbibe & unwind with wine @ 5." *Have you ever heard the saying: "It's five o'clock somewhere?"* If you are not familiar with this expression, it is often uttered when someone is partaking of an alcoholic beverage at a time typically reserved for not drinking such a libation. For example, it is 10 a.m. and a woman has arrived at the airport to catch a plane to her favorite vacation spot in Negril, Jamaica. After summoning the bartender to her table, she orders a tall frosty Sam Adams beer and shot of tequila. As the bartender sets the drinks in front of her, she laughs, then says to her husband as she starts sipping the beer, "I guess it is five o'clock somewhere!" Like this woman, people often say those words to justify why they are drinking an alcoholic beverage so early in the morning.

There actually is something positive about people taking time to drink an alcoholic beverage with close acquaintances around 5 p.m. In fact, some researchers have found that is a custom practiced by many people who are the healthiest and live the longest in the world. Here is how it works.

As you have learned, the "Blue Zones" are the five places on earth where people are the healthiest and live the longest. Except for the Seventh-day Adventists in Loma Linda California, around the 5 o'clock hour (or thereabouts), most of the globe's healthiest and oldest citizens stop what they are doing to hang out with their closest family, friends, or colleagues. Together, the close-knit groups participate in a ritual of consuming one to two glasses of their favorite libations and socialize together.

Individuals consume an alcoholic or nonalcoholic beverage that best suits their palate. It can be a white wine, water, sangria, pina colada, fruit juice, a carbonated beverage, hard liquor like vodka, gin, or rum, or a mixed drink like a Moscow Mule . . . you get the picture!

While the social distancing requirements called for in the response to the COVID-19 pandemic rendered individuals unable to physically come together and practice Principle 3, it did not stop them from doing so in a remote or virtual setting. Creating a recurring "Imbibe and unwind with wine @ 5" video chat via services like Zoom, Skype or FaceTime is a fantastic way to continue this ritual when it is impossible to meet others face-to-face. The important thing is to continue practicing this routine to signal the end of a stressful day, wind down, and "de-stress from stress" with a supportive group of family and friends.

There is an added benefit when people get together late in the afternoon if their drink of choice is red wine. While there is some controversy over whether it is advantageous for people to drink alcohol in moderation, there are many who tout the benefits of drinking red wine. Here is what a wine expert has to say about the health benefits of red wine.

Meet wine expert & entrepreneur Rebecca Beraldi

Rebecca Beraldi is owner of the popular Beacon Hill Wine and Gourmet store (www.beaconhillwine.com) located in Melrose, Massachusetts. Their outstanding customer service and wide selection of wines makes it one of my favorite places to purchase wine. She explains the benefits and science behind consuming red wine: "Red wine has been shown to not only be a great beverage to drink, but also has some medicinal advantages. It contains resveratrol which is an antioxidant. Resveratrol helps the body to better absorb beneficial plant-based antioxidants."

In his book, *The Blue Zones Solution: Eating and Living Like the World's Healthiest People*, Dan Buettner elaborates on the benefits of drinking red wine:

> "People who drink--in moderation--tend to outlive those who don't. (This does not mean you should start drinking if you do not drink now.) People in most Blue Zones drink one to three glasses of red wine per day, often with a meal and with friends. Wine has been found to help the system absorb plant-based antioxidants, so it especially complements a Blue Zone diet. These benefits may come from resveratrol, an antioxidant specific to red wine. But it may also be that a little alcohol at the end of the day reduces stress, which is good for overall health. In any case, more than two to three glasses a day for women and men, respectively, shows adverse health effects."[51]

One of the best red wines to drink

One of the best red wines you can drink is Sardinian Cannonau, if you can find it in your part of the world. The premier red wine that is drunk by one of the healthiest and longest-living groups of people is from the island of Sardinia, the second-largest island in the Mediterranean Sea (after Sicily and before Cyprus). It is in the Western Mediterranean, south of Corsica.

---

[51] Dan Buettner, *Blue Zones Solutions: Eating and Living Like the World's Healthiest People*. (Washington, DC: National Geographic Society, 2015), 177-178.

Cannonau is made from the grenache grape, and the long-living people of Sardinia imbibe small glasses of it daily. It has about two or three times more flavonoids (which are great for scrubbing arteries) than other wine varieties.

I first discovered Sardinian Cannonau red wine in a store in Cambridge, Massachusetts, called City Liquors. More wine stores are carrying Sardinian Cannonau wines and here are a few brands I can recommend:

- Costera Argiolois
- Cannonau Di Sardegna Vigna di Isallle Cantina Dorgali
- Sargenia (Sardinai) Cannonau

Photo by: MRAF
Sardinian Cannonau red wine

Hot Tip: Moderation every day is the key

When practicing this healthy aging tactic to "imbibe and unwind with Wine @ 5," remember that *moderation, every day,* is the key. Only allow yourself to unwind and imbibe with one to two glasses of alcohol per day.

The key here is the words "per day." This is not a cumulative thing where you can skip a day and catch up by partaking of what you missed *and* your daily intake on another day. Okinawans enjoy drinking a special sake, Awamori, only made in Okinawa.

For example, to consume your allotment of a maximum 14 glasses of wine in a week, you cannot drink one on Monday and another on Tuesday, take a three-day break, and then guzzle down the remainder of your 12 glasses over the weekend.

Principle 4: Shake Off Stress

Researchers consumed with studying how people grow old and stay healthy agree upon one thing. Stress is not a friend of healthy longevity. It is of extreme importance to find ways to "shake off stress" because:

> **"Chronic stress is a Goliath-sized enemy of
> growing old and staying healthy."**
> **-MRAF**

Dangers of uncontrolled stress

Experts underscore that severe and repeated stress can cause death because it weakens the immune system. Stress contributes to viral and bacterial infections to degenerative diseases like:

- Asthma
- Cancer
- Cardiovascular disease
- Diabetes
- Hypertension
- Inflammatory bowel disease
- Ulcers

Stress also leads to an increased risk for autoimmune disorders such as:

- Lupus

- Multiple sclerosis
- Rheumatoid arthritis and more

To learn more about the devastating effects of stress on aging, I reviewed many research studies. Many concluded that Okinawans are all-star players when it comes to overcoming stress and preventing it from penetrating their lives. In addition to hard-core empirical data and research about the role that stress plays in how we age, I traveled to Okinawa and interviewed Okinawans and others living there who confirmed that Okinawans generally do not let stress dominate their lives.

I often witnessed an interesting dynamic when I had healthy longevity conversation with Okinawans. During our chats, many would declare, almost out of nowhere, that "Okinawans *do not get stressed*!" The researcher and writer in me had to probe further when they uttered such unbelievable comments. I would follow up and in a truly probing tone say, "I know you've said that Okinawans don't experience stress, but is that *really* true?"

At this point, invariably their responses would become even more adamant. It was clear that they wanted to make sure that it was drilled into my head that yes, they were saying and believed in their conviction that "Okinawans do not have stress!" You will learn more about why Okinawans feel they do not get stressed later in the book.

Stress-resistant personalities

Aside from Okinawans, there are people who do generally seem immune to stress. Experts such as Dr. Margery Silver and Dr. Thomas Perls, directors of the New England Centenarian Study, cite the ability of people to cope with adversity as a factor that contributes to longevity. They have coined the term *stress-resistant personalities* to describe people who possess the ability to resist stress. Many point to the stress-resistant personality traits of Okinawans as one of the reasons they were able to come out of situations as horrendous as what they experienced during WWII.

Sleep and healthy longevity

When people are over-stressed, they may find it difficult to sleep. Did you know that getting enough sleep can impact your ability to live a long and healthy life? As part of your routine to "shake off stress," do not forget to get adequate sleep. To do so, make sure you are practicing these healthy sleeping techniques from Harvard Medical School's *Healthbeat*:

> "There are some simple things you can do to make it easier to fall asleep, and to help ensure that the sleep you get is high quality. One of those is to make your bedroom as quiet as possible. You can reduce or disguise noises that can interfere with sleep by:
>
> • using earplugs
> • decorating with heavy curtains and rugs, which absorb sound
> • installing double-paned windows
> • adding "white noise" either by purchasing a device designed specifically to provide this kind of steady hum, running a fan, or purchasing CDs or downloading apps that provide soothing sounds."[52]

Principle 5: Get in the Groove and Move

The next of MRAF's "8 Healthy LongevityPrinciples" is "Get in the Groove and Move." People who live a sedentary life with little exercise or natural movement tend to die younger than those who adopt an attitude to "get in the groove and move." This technique includes finding more activities to keep the body moving in an effortless, just-part-of-my-life routine.

People who "get in the groove and move" live longer and are not necessarily hiring costly personal trainers or visiting exotic spas. They simply employ natural activities to keep moving. Here are some ways to build "Get in the Groove and Move" activities into your life:

---

[52]   Harvard Medical School, *Focus on Sleep* (Issue #2 of 5 in an email series), January 21, 2020. health.harvard.edu.

Walk Outside. Why not take a stroll outside and take time to enjoy nature's surroundings? Look at and smell fragrant flowers and soak up some vitamin D from the sun. In Chatan, Okinawa, where I lived, people love to take a leisurely stroll, brisk jog, or bike ride at the Sunabee Wall on the East China Sea. Walking the beaches and collecting shells, sea glass, and rocks on just about any island or body of water is delightful to me. I especially love the beaches of Okinawa, Negril (Jamaica), Cape Cod and Martha's Vineyard (Massachusetts). (I call it "My Vineyard" since my name is Martha!)

Walk Inside. In New England, our brutal winter weather can make it almost impossible to even think about walking outside. Some of my relatives in the southern part of the USA and friends in Okinawa also have problems walking outside and don't do so due to brutal summer heat. Do not be sidetracked when the elements are not ideal. Simply try "getting in the groove and moving" by walking inside in places like shopping malls.

Stroll Around Town. Some cities and towns world-wide are actively striving to be "Age-Friendly and Walkable" Cities. They have structured their physical environments so that people can move naturally by walking freely in areas of their communities and not necessarily have to drive. Whether you live in a formally designated Walkable City or not, take a stroll around your neighborhood and enjoy the sights and sounds as you get in some exercise by walking.

The Italian/Mediterranean Tradition of Strolling. This is a time during the early evening where family and friends in Italy and other Mediterranean countries take time to be "out and about" in their towns. In Spain, it is known as the "paseo," and in Italy, the "passeggiata." Every generation participates. Some adults use it to relax and imbibe at five with an aperitivo at "happy hour." This tradition serves as a fantastic way to transition from a day at work and destress from stress.

Run/Jog or Walk/Run. These cardiovascular activities will do wonders to keep you healthy and pump up a positive mood. Diehard runners often get that "runner's high" and feel exhilarated after running. I have lived in Boston where many dedicated runners take the sport to the next level by running the Boston Marathon or shorter 5K and 10K races.

Gardening. Many older Okinawans garden year-round and use the bountiful fruits and vegetables of their labors to stay healthy with fresh, naturally produced foods.

Bicycling can be a pleasurable way to move and groove. Many cities and towns have also installed special bike lanes on their roads so that bicyclists are safe while navigating their way around the terrain.

Sitting on the floor playing with children or grandchildren. What goes down, must come up. If you sit on the ground, somehow you must stand up again and that is great exercise and natural movement!

Enjoy Water Sports like Swimming, Scuba Diving, and Snorkeling. What better way to both get exercise and relieve stress than by doing activities in any body of water? Moving in and around a pond, lake, river, or ocean can be an enjoyable, stress-reducing, and relaxing way to be active and keep yourself calm and centered. Bring the kids along for family fun.

Hiking. Being out in nature has a way of calming many people. Hiking provides a mechanism to exercise and enjoy the beauty that nature brings.

Dancing. I love to dance and to help get in the groove and move, I create my own playlists of my favorite songs, and then dance around in my house for thirty minutes to an hour. Not only do I get exercise by doing something I love, often I can get other chores done as I boogie down.

All of these are great ways to build "Getting in the Groove and Moving" into your life to increase your years on this earth.

Component III: LB2: Love. Be Loved. Belong.

The third component of MRAF's 8 Healthy Longevity Principles that you must practice if you want to achieve healthy longevity, is:

LB2: Love. Be Loved. Belong.

The L stands for **LOVE** and the B2 is **BE LOVED** and **BELONG**.

The ability for people to express unconditional love to others, as well as to adore themselves, is also a reason why people live longer and stay healthy. As the saying goes,

"Begin by loving yourself or you can't truly love or help others."

Importance of relationships and human connectedness

During the age of COVID-19, everyone interested in healthy aging had to severely curtail physical AND social contact with others. Practicing "social distancing" became the rule. I believe the term "social distancing" is a misnomer and the term "physical distancing" should be utilized instead. It is true that in a pandemic situation, individuals must limit in-person contact and physical connection with others. It is important, however, that while people must "socially distance" themselves, they MUST avoid being "socially distant" to other mortals.

"Practice social distancing but don't become socially distant from others!"
-MRAF

No man or woman is an island. People who grow old and stay healthy take special care to fight isolation by nurturing relationships and surround themselves with positive people. If less face-to-face and more virtual encounters are the norm, it is also important to steer away from negative electronic socializing. Make sure that your cyberspace human connectedness leaves you feeling awesome, not awful. Monitor your virtual interactions on Twitter, Facebook, Instagram, LinkedIn, TikTok and other social media platforms.

Scientists and medical experts understand that interpersonal relationships have a significant impact on a person's well-being and ability to ward off diseases. Having an optimistic and giving approach to life pays dividends. In addition, finding connectedness through loving relationships is essential to healthy aging. Harvard Medical School-educated and world-renowned doctor Dean Ornish is a medical trailblazer. Thousands of people worldwide have completed his Ornish Programs, which are so medically effective that major insurance carriers accept his patients for payment. He speaks of the potent and powerful influence of love on healthy longevity:

> **"I am not aware of any other factors,-- not diet, not smoking,**
> **not exercise, not stress, not genetics, not drugs, not surgery—**
> **that has a greater impact on our quality of life, incidence**
> **of illness, and premature death from all causes."**
> **– Dean Ornish[53]**

The healthiest and longest-living people place tremendous emphasis on the quality of their human relationships. They believe that people must stick together through the trials and tribulations of life and support each other. John Robbins provides some startling research findings about the need to create strong social connections if you want to win at the longevity game. He writes:

> "No one familiar with my earlier work will be surprised that I am interested in how our diets and exercise can help us to live long and healthy lives. But they might be surprised by some of my findings, including the great emphasis I am now placing on strong social connections. I have learned that the quality of the relationships we have with other people makes a tremendous difference to our physical as well as emotional health. Loneliness, I discovered in my research, can kill you faster than cigarettes. And by the same token, intimate relationships that are attending and life-affirming can have enormous and even miraculous healing powers."[54]

B2 = Be Loved by Others

Many people who remain healthy as they age believe that their success is not measured by the amount of money and things they possess, but by the quality of the relationships and amount of love and support in their

---

[53]   Dean Ornish, *Love and Survival: The Scientific Basis for the Healing Power Of Intimacy* (New York: Harper Collins, 1998), 3.

[54]   John Robbins, *Healthy at 100:* (2007), xix.

lives. They understand that the key to procuring a fulfilled life is to be surrounded by loving positive people. This includes their relationships with biological and adoptive family members. In addition, their love and support extend to friends, colleagues, individuals where they live, and those in their spiritual and religious communities.

Okinawans love to love others. As you may recall from earlier in the book, they adhere to a saying called:

Ichariba chode
(pronounced: E-cha-rE-ba-chO-de)

**"Though we meet, but once, even by chance,
we are friends (or like family) for life."**

This phrase is widely used in Okinawa. It expresses the sentiment that everyone you meet (including random, brief encounters) is your friend/family member forever. Ichariba chode illustrates the warm, giving, and loving Okinawan Spirit.

B2 = Belong

While you must give love to others, you cannot forget to **love yourself.** Said another way,

"Love and let others love you in return!"

The second "B" stands for "Belong." Letting others love you in return creates a sense of belonging. People who desire healthy longevity belong to certain organizations and communities of like-minded individuals. They often become active participants in:

- the communities where they live, to make them stronger and more livable for people from all generations and walks of life, and in
- faith-based religious and/or spiritual communities comprised of others who share similar beliefs and practices related to their brand of faith.

There is strong evidence that participation in these faith-based, religious, or spiritual communities can contribute to healthy longevity and add years to your life. How many more years can your participation in a faith-based organization bring you? Keep reading as the answer will be revealed further in this chapter, when you will learn about the eighth principle practiced by the world's longest-living people.

Who is healthier: Divorced, married, separated, or single people?

How would you answer this question? If you said that married people tend to be the healthiest, you are *right*! There is substantial scientific and medical evidence that people who are involved in long-term relationships, particularly those who are committed and loving, live longer than individuals who are single, separated, or divorced. According to expert Dan Buettner,

> *"Committing to a life partner can add up to three years of life expectancy."*[55]

Numerous studies reach the same conclusion—married people simply live longer and die less frequently from practically every major cause of death than single, divorced, widowed, or separated people. Research also points out that this is particularly true for men.

Importance of sexual health as we age

Sexual health is an important part of any committed relationship. Studies have proven that centenarians and supercentenarians are generally sexually active throughout most of their lives. They do not tend to linger with prolonged illnesses, but die quickly, only after a brief period of ill health. The added benefit for them that experts have revealed is that many die swiftly and sometimes after having *sex*! To that, I say, "*Wow* and what a way to leave this earth!"

---

[55]   Dan Buettner, **www.bluezones**.com (Accessed April 18, 2018).

B = Belong to Supportive Communities and Groups

"No man or woman is an island. To grow old and be healthy you must fight isolation, surround yourself with positive people and belong to groups that are full of those like-minded individuals."
-MRAF

To achieve healthy aging, examine your environment and the people around you. Several people I know (including my mother) reinforced this notion when they said:

"You are the people you keep. Birds of a feather flock together."

Some also use this phrase in an even more direct way and proclaim:

"You are the people you keep *and* sleep with!"

These phrases underscore the need to be cautious when belonging to groups and to be aware that both the people and the environment in which you live have an impact on your ability to live longer and healthier. An important part of belonging centers around making family and friends a priority.

Principle 6: Family & Friends First

The sixth principle that people employ to win at the healthy longevity game is to ALWAYS put family and friends first. The Merriam-Webster dictionary defines "family" as: **1 a :** the basic unit in society traditionally consisting of two parents rearing their children; *also* **:** any of various social units differing from but regarded as equivalent to the traditional family; **2 :** a group of individuals living under one roof and usually under one head: HOUSEHOLD; **3 a :** a group of persons of common ancestry : CLAN.

Those who achieve healthy longevity believe in creating and being a part of strong family structures as described above. This often means keeping aging parents and grandparents nearby or living inside their homes. People who age and remain healthy passionately believe that the key to procuring a fulfilled life is to be surrounded by those who reciprocate their love and are not just takers or leeches, interested in getting something from them but not giving anything positive in return.

Adopted/Chosen Nonbiological Family

Family relationships which lead to healthy longevity can be with biological or adoptive/chosen family members. People become connected to members of nonbiological families for many reasons. Sometimes they are literally adopted by nonrelatives after being abandoned by a biological family. Others have families that are so dysfunctional it becomes difficult, if not impossible, to maintain healthy and constructive relationships with them. Some people are separated from relatives by geographical distance. For example, I live in the Boston area and my relatives live in a variety of places scattered around the USA. While I love my biological family dearly, I have also cultivated relationships with other families in my area.

These "adopted" families are as close to me as my biological family. My dear friends Darryl, Juliette, Ellie, D'Anna and Danielle Mayers are a case in point. For decades, we have shared great memories and they often welcome me into their home on special holidays like Christmas and Thanksgiving when I am unable to visit biological family members.

Photo by MRAF
Celebrating special occasions with my adopted Mayers
family: Danielle, Darryl, Juliette, and D'Anna

Sharing holidays and leisure time with family can be greatly beneficial to everyone. When families establish and pass traditions to children it may help to sustain them through good and bad times throughout their lives. Family activities also provide a mechanism for children to bond with their elders. My mother was a huge fan of celebrations and bringing family and friends together daily, but especially on major holidays. She started several family traditions that are still practiced by me, and I have passed on to many of our heirs. Because of her influence, generations of my family members have continued her tradition of being big celebrants of birthdays and holidays like Christmas, Easter, and Thanksgiving.

Photo by: Rob Oechsle
Family carp-flying on holiday in Okinawa

At Christmas time, my mom loved involving her children in making family favorite recipes like her Congo Square Brownies. It is a light-colored brownie (some call it a "Blondie") that is made using a technique that allows the brownie to stay a blonde color while the semisweet morsels inside stay intact and do not melt. Every Thanksgiving and Christmas, I apprenticed under her and learned this technique. I have taught countless generations of family members how to make Congo Squares.

Family reunions are also a great time to bring families together. My family, which is scattered throughout the United States, holds a family reunion and graduation celebration in the summer. At this special occasion, everyone from children to elders looks forward to attending as we reacquaint ourselves with each other. We also use this planned family time to honor any member of the family who has graduated from an educational institution that year. This has included relatives who are moving from preschool to first grade as well as those finishing high school, college, medical, and law school. My parents, like the people in Okinawa, transmitted social customs that bind together generations of my family members in a positive way. For the summer of 2020, since we could not physically get together during the COVID-19 pandemic, we did the next best thing and started a new tradition of a Zoom Family Reunion Meeting. We were practicing staying "socially distanced without being socially distant!"

In both Okinawa and Japan, there are several holidays where family members come together for healthy intergenerational fun. Usually in October, they celebrate an entire sports day event called Undōkai at Japanese elementary schools. Whether you are age 1 or 101, for a day you can participate in community-wide sports activities that are often staged in workplaces or schools. These events not only build up family and team camaraderie, but help participants get in the groove and move.

In Okinawa, people *really* know how to have a good time with close family, friends, and even strangers. One popular fun activity pre-COVID-19 was to go out to a karaoke bar (karaoke is a Japanese term that means "empty orchestra"). There were karaoke bars on just about every other corner in my hometown of Chatan, Okinawa, and other places in Japan. Maybe it is "the Okinawa in me," but I adore karaoke and go whenever I can. One of my favorite karaoke spots near Boston is JJ Grimsby in Stoneham, Massachusetts. For many years, my friends have thrown me a karaoke birthday party at that venue.

The kajimaya celebration for people aged 97 years young

In Okinawa when someone reaches 97 birthdays, the entire town treats the person as a hero or shero and holds a special kajimaya celebration. Yes, if you can hit the old age lottery, you will be the toast of the town on Okinawa. In many towns, 97-year-old honorees are still spry, and are treated like royalty and celebrities. Sometimes parades are held where that person is carted around in an open car. Other festivities are held in their honor. Some who attend a kajimaya event want to share in the good luck and superpower of the older person. They call this "ayakaru," which translates into "sharing in the good luck of a person." Celebrants try to shake hands with, touch, or partake in a cup of sake received from the esteemed elder.

The importance of lifelong friends

Like family and committed relationships, having long-term friendships can contribute to longevity. Experts have found that creating social support via friendships helps to reduce stress. Friends can also provide a strong social network to help people achieve and keep healthy behaviors. Okinawans have created a system of friendship that has been widely studied and proven to be extremely successful in helping people to live longer and healthier lives. It is called a *moai* and is typically comprised of about five people who literally vow to support each other for life—through the good, bad, ups and downs.

Individuals in the moai band together for a common purpose of supporting each other. This means emotional, physical as well as financial support. If someone falls on hard times and is need of financial support through a loan or a "No worries, I don't need you to pay me back" gift, they are there for each other. Moai provide a support network that lets people know that regardless of life's downs, someone in their moai will be ready to help.

Moai generally stay as an intact group, but people may move in and out of it depending upon their life circumstances. They also use each other to share life experiences. These social interactions become somewhat of a therapy session and a great way to alleviate stress and tension.

How does *moai* work?

To better understand how the special *moai* friendship system works, see this explanation from the authors of the *Okinawa Program*:

> "Essentially, a *moai* is a group of friends, relatives, workmates or cohorts that get together regularly for purposes of reciprocal support. This support is at once financial, emotional, and social. When a *moai* is formed, everyone agrees on a certain amount of money to be brought to each meeting by each member…At each meeting, one of the members (whoever needs it the most) receives that [which is collected.]…When each member has had his or her turn as recipient, the process starts anew. *Moai*, which have been referred to as the 'people's banks," are not formed indiscriminately. The members always have something in common. They might work in the same occupation, or be old school chums, childhood friends, relatives or from the same hometown."[56]

Photo by: MRAF
Trinity Church Boston

---

[56] Suzuki et al., *The Okinawa Program*, (2001), 284.

Let Your Little Light Shine Higher

The eighth and final component of MRAF's "8 Healthy Longevity Principles" is "Let your little light shine higher." This component is about what the oldest and healthy people in the world do to give back to the world by finding their purpose in life. Once it is discovered, they implement it, thereby letting their little light of hope shine in the world. By taking these actions they seek to stay positive and remain faithful to those around them as well as to a higher power that helps them better navigate better through the tribulations of life.

While conducting research for this book, I was struck by the impact that faith-based, religious, or spiritual practices and organizations have on successful aging. There are major benefits for those people who have a belief in a higher being. People gain longevity points if they believe that such an entity exists and is a constant source of inspiration, healing, and support. Believing, obeying, and trusting (what I call BOT) in such a higher being or force is a common thread for healthy longevity winners of the Blue Zones. Here are a few other startling revelations about this concept.

Spirituality/Attending faith-based services increases life expectancy

Several researchers proclaim that there are longevity advantages to anyone who participates in a faith-based or religious/spiritual organization of like-minded people. Here is what some have found:

> **"Attending spiritual, religious or faith-based services four times a month will add 4-14 years of life expectancy."**[57]

Experts indicate that it does not make *any* difference relative to a person's religious sect, denomination, affiliation, or allegiance. This includes, but not is limited to people who are:

- Buddhists
- Christian

---

[57] The Blue Zones, www.thebluezones.com (Accessed April 18, 2018).

- Confucian
- Jewish
- Muslim
- Seventh-day Adventists
- Taoist

When I learned of the statistic above, I immediately wanted to know, what is the exact definition of religion and spirituality? Dr. Kenneth R. Pelletier defines spirituality versus religion in his classic book, *The Best Alternative Medicine.* He states that spirituality is: "An inner sense of something greater than oneself, a recognition of a meaning of existence."[58]

Dr. Pelletier further defines religion as: "The outward expression of spiritual impulses, in the form of a specific religion or practice…a diminished focus on self: a feeling of love that leads to acts of compassion, empathy, gratitude; and the experience of inner peace." Dr. Pelletier concludes that spirituality is "inherently enriching," and "eminently conducive to health and well-being."

Photo by: MRAF
Asakusa Jenin (Shrine), Tokyo, Japan

---

[58]   Kenneth R. Pelletier, *The Best Alternative Medicine* (New York: Simon & Shuster, 2000).

Fodor's notes: "In Japan, Buddhism and Shintoism have enjoyed a comfortable coexistence since the former arrived from China in the sixth century."[59]

The world's longest-living and healthiest people are strong believers in helping others to blossom and shine. It is believed that before you can help others to make their lights shine, you must first learn how to best let your personal light shine in the world. This brings us to Principle 8.

Principle 8: Find your IKIGAI (reason for being!), then live your dreams daily

In the next chapter, you will learn about Principle 8 and how to ignite your unique light that is your reason for being or what the Okinawans call "Ikigai" (Reason for Being!) and why you wake up in the morning. In the pages ahead, you will learn more about Ikigai and discover four simple questions you can ask to find yours. You will also learn why it is important to not just dream your dreams, but to live them daily.

---

[59] Brett Bull et al., *Fodor's Travel Japan* (New York: Fodor's Travel, a division of Penguin Random House, 2016), 123.

CHAPTER 6:

How Can I Finally Find MY Ikigai (Reason for Being!)?

Photo by Rob Oechsle
Peak of IE Island set on fire by the sun

Principle 8: Find Your Ikigai (Reason for Being!), Then Live Your Dreams Daily

O kinawa, Japan, has more healthy people 110 years and older than anywhere in the world. One of their keys to long life is to find their Ikigai (reason for being/waking up!). In this chapter you will discover four powerful questions to help you FINALLY find YOUR IKIGAI.

WHAT IS IKIGAI?
(REASON FOR BEING/ WAKING UP!)

Photo by: Rob Oechsle
Girl Under a Mushroom Rock

An essential element to achieving healthy longevity
is to find what the Okinawans call:

IKIGAI
(pronounced EE-key-guy)

IKIGAI translates to "Reason for Being/Waking Up!"
IT IS A TERM DERIVED FROM TWO JAPANESE WORDS:

"iki" meaning "life or alive," and
"gai" which is a derivative of "kai" meaning
"worth, value, effect or benefit."

The Okinawan word Ikigai means the reason you wake up in the morning. What is your purpose, your reason for being, on this earth? After you find your Ikigai, you will be thrilled to wake up and complete work that adds worth and value to people around the globe.

Studies have discovered that one element which contributes to Okinawans' longevity is that they work hard to discover their life's purpose. Individuals usually find their Ikigai by answering four powerful questions, which you will learn more about later in this chapter.

The concept of Ikigai originated in Okinawa but is not exclusive to it. All the "Blue Zones" (the five places where people live the longest and are the healthiest in the world) have a similar idea. For example, the French call it "raison d'etre" and individuals from the Nicoya Peninsula of Costa Rica say, "Plan de vida." Regardless of the term, Ikigai is about doing exactly what you were sent to accomplish on earth. It is what propels individuals to feel satisfied, fulfilled, and at peace.

Ikigai is about giving back

Ikigai is not a selfish or negative thing. It is about giving back. The motivation for individuals to find their Ikigai is not to acquire more wealth and riches but to help others succeed in life and at work.

> **"With Ikigai, you are striving to make a positive, memorable difference in the world and help others do the same!"**
> **-MRAF**

The Okinawans believe that everyone has an Ikigai. ONLY the individual, however, can define and discover it. As the old proverb goes, **"Not your mama. Not your daddy. Not your sisters. Not your brothers. But YOU. YOU. YOU. YOU. YOU!"**

Ikigai Examples

Because individuals who have found their Ikigai are doing what they love to do and are good at doing, they wake up thrilled and ready to start their day. A person's Ikigai can be something simple. For others, it is about performing enormous and complex miracle work in the world. Here are a few examples of Ikigai:

- Sharing knowledge with children and grandchildren about what they can do to stay healthy and live longer.
- Doing an outstanding job at work, then spending quality time at home with family and friends.
- Teaching science, technology, engineering, and math (STEM) subjects to students so they can procure meaningful jobs.
- Caring for elderly nursing home patients in hospices.
- Conducting research to cure cancer, diabetes or prevent pandemics from spreading.
- Connecting others through party planning so they have fun in life.
- Planting and caring for a garden that will supply fresh and nutritious vegetables and fruits to lower-income communities.
- Combatting global warming.
- Picking up litter off beaches.
- Bringing diverse people together and working to eliminate racism and sexism.
- Volunteering at a local orphanage to help young children know they are loved.
- Taking great care of aging parents and driving them to medical appointments.

Incredible things happen when you discover your Ikigai

Many who find their Ikigai report that amazing things happen in their lives. They report experiencing:

- A newly discovered meaning and purpose to everyday living.
- A reason for waking up thrilled, happy, elated, joyous and more fulfilled in their personal lives and at work.
- An increased positive and optimistic world outlook and belief that every day brings a new adventure to be explored.
- A desire to be alive and participate in what the universe has to offer as each new day provides a golden opportunity for them to fulfill their Ikigai.

Ikigai adds years to life

Renowned "Blue Zones" researcher Dan Buettner states: "Research has shown that knowing your sense of purpose is worth up to seven years of extra life expectancy."[60]

Answer four questions to find your Ikigai

The secret to finding Ikigai lies in an individual's ability to answer only four questions. While this seems relatively easy, for some it is a daunting task that presents major challenges.

Here are two models (see Figure 6-1 and Figure 6-2) which lay out what the four powerful and life-changing questions to help determine your Ikigai, or "reason for being!/waking up."

[60] Dan Buettner, *Blue Zones Solutions: Eating and Living Like the World's Healthiest People* (Washington, DC: National Geographic Society, 2015), 20.

Figure 6-1

FINALLY FINDING MY IKIGAI
(Reason for Being/Waking Up!)

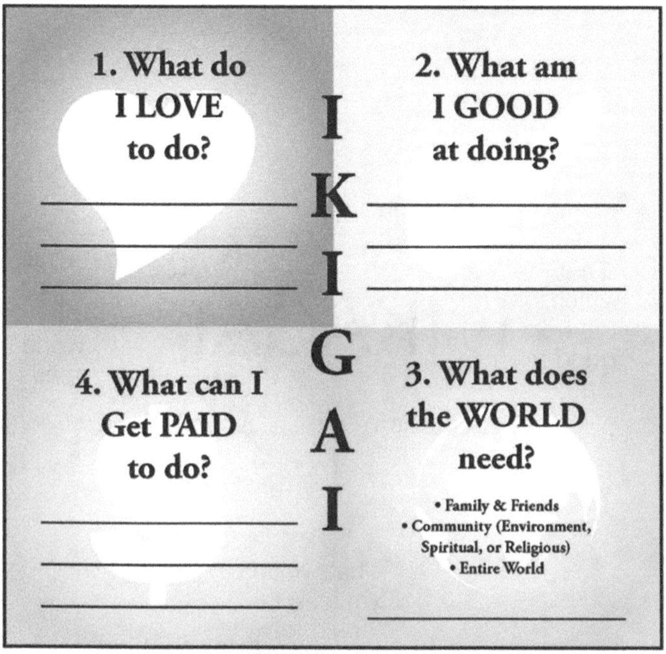

© OKI ME LLC. Martha RA Fields
IKIGAI: (Pronounced EE-kee-guy) Okinawan term meaning Reason for Being/Why you Wake Up?
Instructions: 1) Fill in Your Answers Above. 2) Then Fill in Below:
What is my IKIGAI?
MY IKIGAI IS _____

A second popular Ikigai model

Figure 6-2 offers a popular Venn diagram that is commonly used to describe Ikigai. In it, the intersecting circles overlap to show the relationships of the four steps to finally finding your Ikigai. As you can see, it creates a type of "Ikigai" alliance.

Figure 6-2

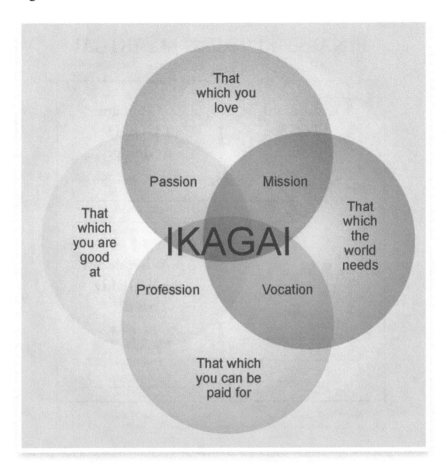

This model recognizes how the four questions intersect around:

- Passion
- Profession
- Mission and
- Vocation

Tips on how to answer the four questions

Here are some tips for those pondering their personal answers to the four thought-provoking IKIGAI questions:

1. What do I LOVE to do?

➤ Do not worry about whether your answers relate to something in your current work or personal life. Jot down things that first come to mind in your job, profession/occupation, or tasks you enjoy doing in your spare time or in your business if you are self-employed.

➤ What do you adore doing most in your personal life and spare time? What things bring joy, fulfillment and make your heart smile? This could be hobbies, volunteer work or leisure time activities.

➤ Do not forget to include things you enjoy in social, political, or faith-based, religious, or spiritual activities. Consider all things you love doing in your response.

2. What am I GOOD at doing?

➤ Please note that what you love to do may be totally different from what you are good at doing. Be realistic when assessing your talents. For example, I love to sing, but my voice is just okay. I could not make a living by singing professionally.

➤ Pat yourself on the back and do not be shy about bragging and writing down what wonderful knowledge, skills, and abilities YOU possess. Go ahead and tastefully toot your own horn about your personal and professional strengths and assets.

3. What does the world need?

To individuals who live the longest and are the healthiest on earth, the word "WORLD" has an overly broad context. It refers to four different things when you are looking to find your Ikigai. Your world includes examining the needs of these groups:

- Family and friends first
- Physical community/communities where you live and work
- Faith-based, religious, or spiritual community
- The entire world

Family and friends first: The people who live the longest and are the healthiest in the world always put their family first. In this context, it can include both your biological, adopted or chosen family. Lifelong friends and those who are a part of your support network should also be considered when replying to this question.

Physical community/communities where you live and work: As discussed, the places where you live and work and the people you surround yourself with can greatly impact your ability to stay healthy and live longer. Ask yourself, am I:

- Working in the right job, profession, work environment and with a boss that is best for me to achieve my Ikigai?
- Taking actions to personally make the physical community where I reside and/or work a better and healthier place?

Faith-based, religious, or spiritual community: Being an active participant in any faith-based, religious, or spiritual community (attending at least four activities per month with fellow members), has numerous benefits for healthy longevity. Like-minded people who share your values, beliefs, and practices can be great support during good and bad times. They can help to reinforce optimism and the knowledge that the possibility still exists for hope, love, and peace on earth.

The entire world: Expand your thinking when it comes to the positive impact you can have on the world. Do your homework and research to determine what exactly the entire world needs to be a better place in which to live. Is it something like world peace, love, happiness, acts of kindness, affordable housing, preventing global warming, information technology, people to find cures for cancer and preventable childhood diseases? The list is endless.

4. How can I get paid?

Remember, Ikigai is ultimately about giving back to others. If you do not have enough financial resources to support yourself and your endeavors, you probably will not be in any condition to help others. Thinking about this Ikigai question truly makes me smile and laugh. Ikigai is such an old concept yet, this fourth and final question seems to be so fresh and relevant in today's world. Consider the following when answering this question:

> Exactly how can I get paid for performing work or services that I love to do, am good at doing, and the world needs? Should I think about starting my own business or consulting rather than working full- or part-time for an organization?
> How will I go about creating this financial opportunity for myself? Who might be of help to me in so doing?

"To sum it up, Ikigai is about what you love to do and are good at doing. What does the world need and how can you get paid to do these things? Your final answers to these four questions come together to reveal your Ikigai (reason for being/waking up). Once found, you will start every day thrilled to have the opportunity to fulfill your personal life's purpose/reason for being!"

- MRAF

Be brutally honest with yourself!

When answering these four questions, d*ig deep into your heart and soul. Be brutally honest with yourself. No one must see the answers you provide unless you want to show them.*

Also, remember that Ikigai is about how you feel, not what you think others would want you to believe. Your Ikigai is not about what your mother, father, significant others, sisters, brothers, friends, enemies, colleagues, co-workers, or anyone else wants you to accomplish. It is about how you want to spend your life adding meaning and purpose to the world!

Ikigai and a bad work situation

Where you work and how you relate to your job, profession, work environment, and the people you interact with are important elements to consider when looking to find your Ikigai. This is especially true if you are working for a bad boss, in a job you despise, or in toxic and unproductive working conditions.

Think about it: many of us spend more waking hours at work in a job(s) than with ourselves, families, or significant others. People whose work aligns with their Ikigai are extremely fortunate. Unfortunately, not everyone possesses that reality. Some abhor their jobs that are not in sync with their Ikigai. This dynamic can spell disaster, especially when negative workday forces spill into their personal lives.

Individuals employed by a horrendous manager should beware. Working for a bad boss can mean horrible things both on the job and at home. A four-letter-word boss (yes, literally the word "boss is spelled" with four letters, but figuratively, it can also cause you to say foul four-letter words) can become a constant figure in one's personal life. That "four-letter-word boss" can reside within the mind of that individual 24 hours a day and a be a mega-negative force, not just on the job, but also at the home dinner table. It can even invade dreams and interfere with positive sleeping patterns.

What if my job is just okay or has nothing to do with my Ikigai?

Sometimes, individuals exist in work environments that are tolerable but have no relevance to their Ikigai. The job does, however, pay the bills and maybe even provides needed money to fulfill that person's Ikigai. If this is the case for you, put your job in perspective. If you can reasonably tolerate the situation, make it work to your advantage. Start looking at your circumstances from this new vantage point.

Instead of it being a source of negativity and anxiety, view your job in a positive light and as a blessing. Dwell on this optimistic perspective. It may not be ideal, but it allows you a means to financially support yourself and family. While it is not your Ikigai, in the end, it allows you the means to fulfill your life's work. In addition, it will provide up to seven years of extra healthy living.

Steps to change horrible job situations

People should take steps to correct their situation if they are working for a bad boss, in a poor working environment, or have lost interest in their occupation or job. The cost and toll these circumstances impose on one's health and ability to live a long and health life are not worth the tradeoff of staying in that horrible situation.

Toxic work situations lead to chronic stress that, if left unchecked, weakens the immune system, and causes a plethora of health problems. Stress-related health conditions include Alzheimer's, anxiety, asthma, cancer, depression, diabetes, hypertension, gastro-intestinal problems, and obesity, just to name a few. In addition, a poor work situation may cause people to lose focus and even prevent them from finding or fulfilling their Ikigai.

When I finally found my Ikigai

You may recall that 52 years after leaving my cherished childhood home in Chatan, Okinawa, I returned to the island's sandy shores on the magnificent East China Sea in 2016. Soon after arriving, I knew exactly why my longing to return and bask in the magic of the island had persisted throughout my life.

I also discovered that so much of what I knew about life and healthy aging I had learned living in Okinawa. As noted, during that trip, I first learned about Ikigai. It was then that I found my Ikigai (reason for being). While it had been staring me in the face the entire time, I had not clearly articulated what it was until I returned to Chatan. Through that powerful experience, I realized that my Ikigai is to:

> "Help people world-wide find life,
> work, and healthy aging success!"

Now that you have learned how to finally find your Ikigai, I hope you will take time to answer the four thought-provoking and life-changing Ikigai questions. This exercise may be the key that unlocks the secrets to your own Ikigai. Once you have identified your reason for being, expect incredible things to happen. You will be on the way to enjoying a purpose-filled life and waking up thrilled every day because you are doing what you:

LOVE to do, are GOOD at doing, the WORLD NEEDS and you are getting PAID to do it!

More tips for answering the Ikigai questions

Here are some tips to consider when answering the four Ikigai questions:

> ➤ Start by finding a place that is quiet and where you are comfortable, and your thinking will not be interrupted or distracted. Try extra-hard to stay focused on completing your task to answer these questions.
>
> ➤ Before answering the questions, do something that can help you concentrate better. This may include listening to music, going outside in nature, sitting on the beach, or taking a walk.
>
> ➤ Be honest with yourself. Stay mindful and keep in the moment. Block out other distractions that may pop into your brain and try to invade your thought process.
>
> ➤ Go with your "gut instinct" when answering the questions. Try hard not to censor the spontaneous thoughts that cross your mind when answering each of the four questions. Do not overanalyze or pass too much judgement on the information that is coming out of your brain. Simply type or write down your thoughts.
>
> ➤ Record everything that comes to mind first when you think about each question. Do not overthink or procrastinate on your responses. *There are no right or wrong answers.*
>
> ➤ The first time you work on this exercise, give yourself a five-minute time limit to answer each question. Write down the immediate things that come to your mind. Then, move to the next question. You can always go back and change or rework your responses.
>
> ➤ There is no specific timeline as to when you will FINALLY find your Ikigai. As mentioned, you may easily locate it, or it may take an enormous amount of time and soul-searching to discover it. Not to worry. It will be made known at the time that is right for you!
>
> ➤ Do not worry about what others may think about your choices. This is your, not their, Ikigai! If it helps, feel free to share your answers

with others; otherwise, keep them to yourself. This is a choice only you can make. Do what feels right for you.

➤ Think about the two Ikigai models (see Figure 6-1 and Figure 6-2) on the previous pages when answering the four questions.

➤ Feel free to start, stop and restart answering your four questions. You might want to start the process then walk away from it. Sometimes it may be necessary to let your answers marinate, then sauté and simmer before you try to finish cooking your Ikigai recipe. Once all your answers are assembled, you will be ready to savor your delicious Ikigai meal.

"Take the necessary time to answer the four questions but make sure you eventually complete them."
- MRAF

DECLARING MY IKIGAI

DIRECTIONS: Based upon what you have learned in this chapter, write your IKIGAI (Reason for Being/Waking Up) below. Remember, there are no wrong answers. It is about what Ikigai means for YOU. You may recall that mine is: "Helping People World-Wide Find LIFE, WORK, and HEALTHY AGING Success!"

<u>WRITE YOUR ANSWER BELOW</u>

MY IKIGAI (REASON FOR BEING/WAKING UP!):

_____

_____

_____

_____

_____

_____

Congratulations on the fantastic accomplishment of FINALLY Finding YOUR IKIGAI!

Photo by: Rob Oechsle
Free Spirit Girl on East China Sea Beach, Okinawa

Best of luck as you start your Ikigai journey!

Now that you have taken time to finally find your Ikigai, start to put into action what you have discovered. Watch for the incredible things that should happen in your life when you are living a purpose-filled life and waking up thrilled every day because you are doing what you:

- LOVE to do,
- Are GOOD at doing,
- Know the WORLD NEEDS and
- You are getting PAID to do it!

In the next chapter, you will find resources to help you continue learning about the medicine, research, and science behind healthy aging.

PART III:

MAKING THE COMPLICATED UNCOMPLICATED: THE MEDICINE, RESEARCH AND SCIENCE (MRS) BEHIND HEALTHY AGING

Part III sorts through the "fake news" to provide proven, evidence-based, and peer-reviewed information about healthy aging. Complex medical and scientific information is presented in an uncomplicated manner along with resources to continue your healthy aging learning.

CHAPTER 7:

Proven Medical, Research & Science (MRS) Facts About Healthy Aging Made Simple

For most of my professional career, I have worked with some of the brightest minds at places like Brown University, Harvard University, Boston University, Northeastern University, and the Massachusetts Institute of Technology (MIT). At age 33, I became a vice president at a Harvard Medical School-affiliated teaching hospital and for decades have consulted to some of the world's top healthcare institutions and corporations. As such, my background dictates that to write this book, I had to understand the anecdotal and hard-core peer-reviewed medical, research, and scientific facts about healthy aging.

To help you better understand these dimensions, this chapter provides insights directly from international experts through their evidence-based and peer-reviewed research, publications, articles, and opinions. Worried you cannot understand such scholarly information because you do not have a medical, science, or research background? No worries. I've uncomplicated this complicated information so you can easily understand what it is and how you can best adapt what is covered to your life.

If, however, you are a numbers or STEM-type person do not be discouraged. I will show you the numbers as well as provide information on the names of some top experts and other resources you can use to validate their findings or wade through the complexities of their research, books, and articles at your leisure. If you want to do more in-depth research on this topic (as I highly recommend), I have also provided information on some of the classic and trending research that I found helpful.

World's top healthy aging experts

In 1987, US President Ronald Reagan, after signing the INF Treaty with Soviet Union General Secretary Mikhail Gorbachev, uttered a Russian proverb: "Trust, but verify." If you are a person who lives by that philosophy, it may be important for you to personally check out some of the facts I have presented. You may also want to conduct your own in-depth research on healthy longevity. The number of world-renowned longevity experts is humongous, so to help get you started on your investigation, I have provided some leads in this chapter.

Below is a condensed list of my favorite experts on healthy aging. These individuals were selected because of their superb, time-tested wisdom on this complex topic. Others may not concur with my picks, but these individuals were of tremendous help throughout my journey to decode and decipher complex data and research. Please note that this is by no means an exhaustive list of the numerous phenomenal experts doing work in the growing and ever-expanding field of healthy longevity.

At the top of my list are three men who are the authors of the highly regarded classic longevity study, *The Okinawa Centenarian Study*. This terrific trio also penned a book that I have mentioned, absolutely adore, and could not stop reading. It is titled, *The Okinawa Program*. Their names are:

- **Makoto Suzuki, MD, PhD**
- **Bradley J. Willcox, MD**
- **D. Craig Willcox, PhD**

The Okinawa Program **is a must-read for anyone interested in obtaining a 35,000-feet overview of the secrets to healthy longevity.** I have read every page of this blockbuster 484-page book. It was first published in 2001, but much of its page-turning information still rings true.

Here is the CliffsNotes version of the impressive credentials of the individuals on my **World's Best Healthy Aging "MRS" Experts List.**

- **Makoto Suzuki, MD, PhD:** Cardiologist and geriatrician, professor emeritus and former director of the Department of Community Medicine at the University of the Ryukyus, Okinawa. Chair, Division of Gerontology, Okinawa International University. Author of *The Okinawa Centenarian Study* and *The Okinawa Program*. Director, Okinawa Research Center for Longevity Science. Author of close to 200 peer-reviewed scientific publications.

- **Bradley J. Willcox, MD**: Author of *The Okinawa Centenarian Study* and *The Okinawa Program*. Physician-investigator in geriatrics, Pacific Health Research Institute and clinical assistant professor in Department of Geriatrics, University of Hawaii, John A. Burns School of Medicine. Principal Investigator U S National Institutes of Health in the funded study *Genetics of Exceptional Longevity in Okinawan Centenarians.*

- **D. Craig Willcox, PhD**: Author of *The Okinawa Centenarian Study* and *The Okinawa Program*. Gerontologist and Medical Anthropologist. Research Associate Harvard University's New England Centenarian Study. Professor, Okinawa Prefectural University.

- **Dan Buettner:** I call him "The Godfather of the 'Blue Zones.'" He is a researcher, inspirational speaker, and author of numerous books, including *The Blue Zones: Second Edition. 9 Lessons for Living Longer From the People Who've Lived the Longest.*

- **John Robbins:** Author of *Healthy 100: How You Can – At Any Age – Dramatically Increase Your Life Span and Your Health Span*. Leading world expert on the dietary link between environment and health.

- **Carol Bates, MD:** Associate Dean for Faculty Affairs and Associate Professor of Medicine at Harvard Medical School. She is a successful and innovative internal medical specialist at Boston's Beth Israel Deaconess Medical Center and has trained many renowned physicians and worked for decades providing stellar care to help patients obtain healthy longevity.

- **T. Colin Campbell**: Biochemist and co-author with his son, Thomas Campbell, II, MD, of *The China Study*. He served as project director of this famous study. The T. Colin Campbell Center for Nutritional Studies bears his name.

- **Michael Greger, MD:** Author of *How Not to Die,* and website ***http:// www.NutritionFacts.org***, a science-based public service. The site features free updates on the latest in nutrition research via articles and thousands of videos on healthy aging.
- **Robert Kane, MD:** Professor, School of Public Health, University of Michigan, and Endowed Chair, Long-term Care and Aging, University of Michigan. Director, Center on Aging and the Minnesota Geriatric Education Center, University of Minnesota, Minneapolis.
- **Hirose Nobuyoshi, MD:** Gerontology expert specializing in mild cognitive impairment, geriatric assessments, and extreme longevity.
- **Dean Ornish, MD:** Cardiologist, researcher, and author. President and founder of Preventative Medicine Research. His "Program for Reversing Heart Disease" has been highly effective for people who experienced heart valve repair, coronary artery, heart or lung bypass or coronary angioplasty or stenting. His renowned INTERHEART Study of more than 29,000 people in 52 countries unveiled nine diet and lifestyle factors responsible for heart attack risks.
- **Thomas T. Perls, MD, MPH:** Assistant Professor of Medicine, Harvard Medical School, and geriatrician. Founder and Co-director of New England Centenarian Study (NECS). Coauthor, *Living to 100: Lessons in Living to Your Maximum Potential at Any Age.* Associate Professor of Medicine and Geriatrics Boston University School of Medicine.
- **Dr. Gianni Pes, MD and Michael Poulain, PhD:** This dynamic duo includes Sardinian medical doctor Pes and demographer Poulain. They were the first to deliver "Blue Zones" data to the world. This pair later worked closely with "Blue Zones" guru Dan Buettner to expand their research to the five places where people live the longest and are the healthiest in the world.
- **Margery Hutter Silver, EdD:** Neuropsychologist, Professor in Psychology at Harvard Medical School, author and Associate Director of New England Centenarian Center. She has served as Co-editor of the *Journal of Geriatric Psychiatry.* Her work centers on the physical health, cognitive abilities, and personalities of centenarians.
- **Andrew Thomas Weil, MD:** Practitioner, researcher, author, and educator of integrative medicine. An advocate for alternative medicine. Served at the University of Arizona College of Medicine as the Lovell-Jones Professor of Integrative Rheumatology, Clinical Professor of Medicine and Professor of Public Health.

Overview of key research studies and healthy aging resources

To make the complicated uncomplicated, I have listed below just a few of the multitude of research studies and resources that I have found to be particularly helpful in understanding the medicine, science, and research behind healthy longevity. They include:

- **The China Study**
- **Framingham Study**
- **New England Centenarian Study**
- **Okinawa Centenarian Study**
- **Okinawa Program**

The China Study

The China Study: The Most Comprehensive Study of Nutrition Ever Conducted, and the Startling Implications for Diet, Weight Loss, and Long-Term Health (2004) is a highly touted study and a *New York Times* bestselling book. It was co-authored by the father/son team of T. Colin Campbell, MD, and Thomas Campbell, II, MD. This study began as a search to uncover the extreme differences in cancer rates within China. It found a strong relationship between consuming animal products and cancer.

The report confirmed the scientific evidence that eating a plant-based diet, with minimal amount of food derived from animals, is ideal. It also found that eating meat from animals can lead to chronic illnesses such as "coronary heart disease, diabetes, leukemia and a multitude of cancers in both children and adults including:

- Brain
- Breast
- Colon
- Esophagus
- Liver
- Lung

- Prostate
- Rectum"[61]

The Framingham Study (the "Framingham Heart Study")

There are three classic studies that have sufficiently correlated overall longevity patterns between children and their parents. They are the:

- Alameda County Study
- "Termite Study"
- The Framingham Study (which took place in Framingham, Massachusetts, not too far from my hometown of Boston)

The Framingham Study (also referred to as the Framingham Heart Study) is a well-respected long-term, multigenerational study. It began over 70 years ago in 1948 as a family-based study of individuals living around Framingham, Massachusetts. It is the longest-running cardiovascular study and involved the testing and examination of some 5,209 participants. Some of the original cohort members are still active members of the study and followed by researchers. Since 1971, it has been conducted at Boston University in partnership with the National Heart, Lung, and Blood Institute. The main research facility is in Framingham, but there are also offices at the Boston University Medical Center.

On its website, www.bu.edu/ths/, the group provides the following information on this important study and states:

> "Much of the earliest scientific evidence of the relationships between cardiovascular disease and smoking, obesity, diabetes, high blood pressure, and high cholesterol... Knowledge of the combined effects of these risk factors, and others, led to discoveries such as the **Framingham Risk Functions**. Physicians and patients throughout the world currently use these functions to estimate, often decades in advance, individual risks for developing specific cardiovascular diseases.

---

[61] Christine Cox and T. Colin Campbell, *The China Project: Revealing the Relationship Between Diet and Disease* (New Century Nutrition, 1996), 69-110.

Other landmark discoveries that came from the study include the protective role of HDL (or "good") cholesterol and the adverse effect of hormone replacement therapy on women's risk for stroke."[62]

New England Centenarian Study

The New England Centenarian Study, according to its website, is "the largest and most comprehensive study of centenarians and their families in the world."[63] It is made up of two landmark studies, the New England Centenarian Study (founded in 1995) and the multi-center Long Life Family Study (established in 2006) and includes five study sites including Boston Medical Center. Here is a summary of key findings:

- "Exceptional longevity runs strongly in families.
- Among centenarians, disability is typically compressed towards at least their early-to-mid-nineties."

See: www.bumc.bu.edu/centenarian/ and New England Centenarian Study: http://www.med.harvard.edu/programs/necs.

The Okinawa Centenarian Study

While I discovered many fantastic research studies on healthy aging, one offers stellar insights into Okinawan longevity. It is the Okinawa Centenarian Study. Based upon significant amounts of scientific documentation, it verifies Okinawa's longstanding and incredible health and longevity records. The three prominent researchers who I discussed earlier in this chapter methodically screened, examined, documented, and analyzed the results of the island's elderly population for over twenty-five years.

---

[62] Boston University School of Medicine and Boston University School of Public Health, "The Framingham Heart Study," https://www.bu.edu/sph/research/framingham-heart-study/. Accessed June 21, 2021.

[63] Boston University Medical Center, "New England Centenarian Study," www.bumc.bu.edu/centenarian/ Accessed June 21, 2021.

Hope conquering aging!

Great strides are being made constantly by experts worldwide. In my own hometown of Boston, Massachusetts, new discoveries are being made at institutions like Harvard Medical School and Boston University Medical School. Dedicated individuals at these institutions are working diligently to better understand healthy aging and advance their missions to provide outstanding research, teaching and patient care. Since new information is constantly evolving, take time to continue exploring information on this topic.

Free resources from the world's top medical experts

Here are some outstanding free electronic resources that can help you in your healthy aging knowledge quest. Sign up on their websites to receive free information from the world's top medical and scientific organizations. These renowned experts can help you to stay on top of changes in healthy longevity issues. Surprisingly, they produce a good amount of helpful and uncomplicated articles that are useful to physicians and scientists as well as to those with little or no scientific or medical knowledge.

Here are some sites I found extremely helpful when I conducted my research for this book. Sign up today for their free newsletters and updates that offer unbelievably useful information that is evidence-based and peer reviewed.

Harvard Medical School and Harvard Health Publishing's HEALTHbeat

Harvard Medical School provides a free resource through their Harvard Health Publishing's **HEALTHbeat**. Their motto is "the most trusted name in online health information." This invaluable resource provides information from the "11,000 doctors and medical researchers of Harvard Medical School," with articles written in a manner that can be understood by the layperson. I highly recommend that if you want to continue learning past this book, signing up for the free HEALTHbeat newsletter would be well worth your time. HEALTHbeat provides free healthy longevity tips and booklets such as ***101 Tips for Top Health*** and ***Aging in Place: How to Live at Home Safely and Independently for as Long as Possible.***

They also offer a paid premier membership, a subscription that adds a plethora of benefits including: "Ask Harvard Dr. Videos," unlimited access to **HEALTHbeat,** health decision guides (you can access the symptoms of 135 health problems), and digital editions of Harvard's bestselling newsletters. For information on these services,

Go to: www.health.harvard.edu/healthbeat.

Journal of the American Medical Association (JAMA)

The *Journal of the American Medical Association* allows a limited number of free downloads on a limited number of articles including those in current issues. Visit this prestigious source of medical research, case studies, articles, resources, and other information to gain knowledge on the latest medical advances.

Go to: www.jamanetwork.com

New England Journal of Medicine (NEJM)

The New England Journal of Medicine also permits a certain number of free downloads of articles each month. This is another fantastic source to stay abreast of the latest healthy aging medical breakthroughs. Visit their website to sign up for limited free access to information.

Go to: www.nejm.org

The *NEJM* also publishes a newsletter that alerts subscribers to the journal's weekly table of contents. For more information,

Go to: nejmtoc@nejm.org

The Journals of Gerontology

This prestigious journal contains informative articles about aging. Check out their special issue titled *Journals of Gerontology Series A: Biological and*

Medical Sciences. It explores "enablers of healthy longevity" as well as the "accompanying opportunities and challenges."

Go to: The Journal of Gerontology Series A https://academic.oup.com/biomedgerontology

Centers for Disease Control and Prevention

The Centers for Disease Control and Prevention is the USA's national health protection agency. They "save lives and protects people from health threats."

Go to: www.cdc.gov

World Health Organization (WHO)

The WHO provides up-to-date health information from around the world. Their mission is to "achieve better health for everyone. Everywhere." They work with 194 member states, across six regions and from more than 150 offices.

Go to: www.who.int.

National Institute on Aging

This organization provides "science-based information on healthy aging." They also provide insights on funding opportunities from the institute and other research and news.

Go to: www.nia.nih.gov.

The National Academy of Medicine's Global Roadmap for Health Longevity

This organization provides "a call to action to understand how individual biology, societal enablers, medical science, and technology could be harnessed to ensure that people worldwide can live longer, healthier, and more fulfilling lives. The potential for increased longevity elevates the importance of our health at all ages."

Go to: www.nam.edu.

Gain More Knowledge: Resources to Continue Your Learning

After reading this book, feel free to quench your thirst for more knowledge by checking out these resources:

- ➤ American Alzheimer's Association: http://www.ALZ.org
- ➤ American Association of Retired Persons: http://www.aarp.org
- ➤ American Cancer Society: http://www.cancer.org
- ➤ American Heart Association: (information on prevention and control of heart disease): http://www.heart.org
- ➤ Mayo Clinic http://www.mayoclinic.org
- ➤ WebMD: http://www.webmd.com
- ➤ Your Disease Risk (this tool, first developed at the Harvard School of Public Health, allows you to find your risk for the twelve most common cancers): https://publichealthsciences.wustl.edu/community-focus/your-disease-risk-assessment-tool/

Check with your physicians and healthcare providers for specific advice

Always consult with your physicians and healthcare providers about your healthcare needs and wants. Please *do not* use the information in this book as a substitute for pursuing personal medical treatment, advice, or diagnosis from your healthcare practitioners.

In the next section, Part IV, you will hear directly from the people who live or have lived in Okinawa. They will provide firsthand insights on why Okinawans are the longest-lived and healthiest people on the planet. They will deliver valuable tips on how to stay healthy and live a long life despite difficulties and setbacks.

PART IV:

YEAH…I LIVED IN OKINAWA: PERSPECTIVES FROM PEOPLE WHO HAVE LIVED THERE

Photo courtesy: Rob Oechsle

Welcome to Part IV, where you will hear directly from the people who call Okinawa home: indigenous Okinawans, Japanese, and people like myself who have had the privilege to reside there. Individuals share their perspectives on how Okinawan longevity works in the lives of real people, and many will utter moving insights about what it is like to live in this healthy longevity Shangri-La.

This chapter also discusses the horrendous experiences that Okinawans endured during and after World War II. Pay attention to what they did to brave the dark storms of death and destruction when close to 200,000 people were killed in a matter of months. Their stories may resonate with those, who during the COVID-19 pandemic, lost nearly everything and those mourning the deaths of loved ones, friends, and colleagues.

"The stories here reveal how despite horrendously hard times, Okinawans picked themselves up from the ashes of evil. Once freed from the jaws of hopelessness and despair, they emerged as winners in the healthy aging game."

Their comments may surprise and even amaze you. You will also hear the voices of individuals who currently live or have lived in Okinawa. This includes those who are from the USA and other parts of the globe as well as people who have served in the Armed Forces there.

CHAPTER 8:

Perspectives from Okinawans and People Who've Lived There

Photo courtesy: Rob Oechsle

I finished the first draft of my manuscript for this book just after the New Year in January 2018. My intuition told me then that one thing I must do before my book could FINALLY be published was to take what I had written back to my beloved people in Okinawa for review.

I felt the urge to get their blessings on what I had written. For some reason, I needed their approval of my account on how they became the world's healthiest and longest-living people. I also wanted to verify from firsthand accounts what my research from the world's top MRS (Medical, Research, and Science) experts had concluded about why Okinawans are the world's healthiest long-lived people.

I longed to get some additional interviews and case studies of real Okinawans and Japanese individuals who would tell me in their own words why they felt Okinawans are the Olympic gold medalists in the "Healthy Longevity Games."

My desire was to return to Okinawa with my final manuscript and not just interview my Okinawan colleagues and friends but also do my first official reading from this book. I put that wish out into the universe, and before I knew it, God granted it.

On February 22, 2018, a cold, wintry day, I boarded an American Airlines plane at Boston's Logan Airport en route to Chatan, Okinawa. That was a super-special date, for it was the birthday of George Washington, the first president of the United States. My mission was to celebrate George Washington's birthday as well as my own and to return to Okinawa with my manuscript in hand.

While I had hoped to be in Okinawa on February 22, the weather had other plans for me. It would not cooperate. The winter of 2017-2018 was one of the worst in the 45+ years that I had lived in Boston. Because of delayed flights, I reached my destination on God's time, not mine. I did not arrive at the Naha, Okinawa airport until February 25, 2018, some three days from when I originally left Boston.

You may recall that I spoke earlier about how long and arduous a journey it can be traveling to Okinawa. Should you ever decide to visit that paradise-like place, remember that you must pack a huge bag of patience for your trip. In my over half-century of traveling to and from Okinawa, I have discovered that it is often likely that the journey will include delays.

I have also learned to enjoy the adventure of the journey rather than curse the delays. The elongated trip has always been well worth the price of reaching Nirvana. My heart smiled big-time when, at around 1:00 a.m., I disembarked from my Japan Airlines Tokyo flight and emerged into the beautiful, orchid-lined Naha Okinawa Airport.

I was so weary after three days of travel. In those early hours, many of the shops and services in the Naha Airport were closed but I could still, however, enjoy viewing the large array of colorful tropical fish swimming in the airport's gorgeous aquarium. I retrieved my bags. Unfortunately, I ran into big trouble when it came to my next step of procuring transportation to the Airbnb apartment I would be staying at in Chatan.

I could not find anyone who could speak English and direct me to some mode of transportation. I was so tired that it did not dawn on me that instead of asking Okinawan people in English if they spoke English, I could use my Google Translator on my iPhone to ask that same question in Japanese. Eventually, I got lucky and ran into a young Okinawan man who graciously helped me find a cab.

As it turned out, he was a teacher at a school in Naha, the capital city of Okinawa. He was with his fellow teachers, headed to the USA to spend some time studying at a school. Like so many Okinawans, he was uber-nice, helpful, and polite. He even introduced me to his colleagues and the esteemed principal of his school. I was so grateful for his assistance because without his help, I probably would not have made it out of the airport.

As I put my weary but happy body into that cab, my heart was smiling big-time as I rode to my studio apartment in Chatan. The location was not far from where I had grown up at Kadena Air Base. After settling into my apartment, I got to explore my beloved Okinawa. On Tuesday, February 28, 2018, I had the opportunity to do my first book reading in Chatan. It was hosted by restaurateur Takuya Nakahashi at the Grill & Bistro Bar Garden, one of several restaurants he owns. The location was literally right around the corner from my apartment. You will read more about this successful businessman in the pages ahead.

In addition to the book reading, I took every opportunity on my trip to speak with Okinawans about my book and solicit their firsthand comments. In so doing, I accomplished my goal to procure the opinions of real Okinawan people, not just what I had learned from the experts. What follows are real-life interviews, profiles, and case studies from people who were born in Okinawa and people who have lived there. You will be introduced to a cross-section of Okinawan society. My interviewees were professionals, entrepreneurs, and average working people. Each person profiled explains (from their firsthand perspective) why they believe that Okinawans live the longest and are the healthiest on the planet. The first profile is a popular businesswoman, Phai Brackett.

liveatphais@gmail.com

Photo courtesy: Phai Brackett

PROFILE: Phai Brackett

Ms. Phai is a phenomenally successful entrepreneur in Okinawa who owns several popular and well-known international businesses. One that I particularly like is called Phai's House of Jade. They sell a wide variety of arts and crafts from Asia, including jade, pearl, and semiprecious stone jewelry, figurines, Asian and Japanese souvenirs and gifts, bone carvings, Vietnamese ceramics, lacquerware, and Chinese porcelain.

Ms. Phai is beautiful inside and out. She possesses incredibly high-octane energy along with personality plus. Her company is known for its upbeat and colorful live online auctions, broadcast from Okinawa to a legion of devoted followers world-wide. Ms. Phai's business is a family affair. She works alongside her loving husband as well as with her loyal assistants, Ms. Ging Martin and her husband, Mike Martin.

Ms. Phai is a true example of the "Okinawan Spirit" in action. We had met through the "Yeah... I lived in Okinawa" Facebook page and I contacted her to see if we might connect while I was in Okinawa. She and I had often commented on each other's posts.

Some people in Okinawa, like those in the Deep South of the United States, do not necessarily like referring to people by their first or last names alone. A title like Miss or Mr. might be added to individual's names when speaking to or about them. Another way that names are presented in Okinawa (as in Japan, more generally) is to put the word "san" at the end of a name. (For example, some people call me Martha-san or Miss Martha.)

Photo courtesy: Phai Brackett
Left to Right: Ging Martin, Phai Brackett and Ryan
Pyke inside Phai's House of Jade in Okinawa

Ms. Phai truly pulled out the red carpet for my arrival and made me feel *so* welcomed. When I got settled in my apartment on Monday, I contacted her to firm up the details on our introductory meeting. We had a lively discussion and she invited me to lunch at her home on Wednesday. I had requested to visit one of her shops and she said she would gladly make sure I could do so.

Remember, this woman did not know me except via a Facebook group. Since I did not rent a car in Okinawa, she offered to pick me up. Our plans, however, got altered, as Ms. Phai and her husband had been traveling off the island and become sick. After apologizing profusely, she offered to send Ms. Ging, her assistant, to pick me up, bring me to her shop, and take me to lunch. Promptly at the designated time, a super-effervescent Ms. Ging picked me up at my apartment. She was very petite, fashionably dressed, and an incredibly warm and hospitable person. We spent several hours together. She took me to one of Ms. Phai's shops located on Camp Foster, a US Marine Corps Base not far from Kadena Air Base. I got to meet Ms. Ging's equally energetic coworkers at Phai's House of Jade.

Upon completing my visit to Ms. Phai's store, Ms. Ging handed me a beautifully packaged gift bag and said that it was a gift from Ms. Phai. Inside was a magnificent heart-shaped jade pendant necklace and earrings set. My eyes welled with tears as I read the note attached, which explained that when someone in Okinawa gives you jade, it is to bring you good luck. While I was shocked and overwhelmed by the unbelievable generosity and kindness of Ms. Phai and Ging to me, a stranger, I should have known better. After all, I was in Okinawa, the place where if you recall, they practice

"Ichariba chode" (E-cha-rE-ba-chO-de)
TRANSLATION: "Though we meet, but once, even by chance, we are friends (or like family) for life."

I did get the opportunity to interview Ms. Phai by phone. When asked **why Okinawans are the oldest and healthiest people on earth**, she replied energetically, "I believe it's mostly because of what is inside of the Okinawan people's hearts and minds. Their hearts are so beautifully pure, and kind and they are mindful of how their actions affect others. It shows in everything they say and do. Oh, how I love Okinawa and its people!"

If you are ever in Okinawa, I highly recommend that you check out Ms. Phai's shop. You will not be disappointed and will probably leave there having purchased, at incredible prices, a multitude of souvenirs and Okinawan goods. You can also participate in one of her live online international auction broadcasts. You will be amazed at the unbelievable prices at these auctions.

For more information, visit:
LIVE AT PHAIS Facebook Page.

https://www.facebook.com/liveat phais/ and www.globuya.com

PROFILE: Kumiko "Kumi" Mituhisa

Photo by: MRAF
Martha and Kumiko Mituhisa in Okinawa

I first met my friend Kumiko "Kumi" Mituhisa in the 2016 Christmas and New Year's holiday season during my first trip back to Okinawa in decades.

On that trip, I stayed at the Hotel Sunset Terrace, nestled within a village in Chatan. It was an ideal location, just 1.5 miles from Sunset Beach, 1.8 miles from Kadena Air Base, and 1.4 miles to Mihama American Village. The famous Sunabe Seawall and boardwalk that meanders along the East China Sea is within walking distance.

Kumi was the concierge and "Jackie of all trades" at the Hotel Sunset Terrace. It was evident that she took pride in making all her guests feel well taken care of while residing at the hotel. Over the years, we have stayed in touch, and she provides me with superb suggestions on must-see attractions in Okinawa.

On my second return visit to Okinawa in February and March 2018, seeing Kumi was high on my list. She very much enjoys spending quality time and making memories with family and friends. Kumi also believes in giving back to her community and making the environment around her safe and clean. She often participates in efforts to remove debris from beaches in Okinawa and encourages friends, family members, and others to do the same. Kumi told me that it is important to make sure they remain clean and pristine for her children and generations to come.

You may recall learning in MRAF's "8 Healthy Longevity Principles" that researchers have found this strong sense of caring about one's physical environment and community is something shared by many people who live long and healthy lives. Kumi's desire to prioritize family and friends and keep them first in her life is also a trait of those who succeed at healthy aging.

On March 1, 2018, I met Kumi at a seaside restaurant directly across from the beach. I asked Kumi **why she thinks Okinawans live such long and healthy lives.** She told me that she believes it is because "they're happy people and get along with each other, and many love dancing and singing." She said, "Okinawans try not to fight each other. Very peaceful."

She also believes that they live longer because of what they eat. She told me that "Okinawans eat lots of vegetables and work hard in their garden to grow them. Natural vegetables. They are very good for you."

As discussed, research has found that those who are successful at healthy aging find ways to naturally, as I say, "Get in the groove and move." Gardening is one method used to accomplish that feat. In addition, the fresh fruits and herbs grown in Okinawan gardens help people to maintain a healthy diet. The highly plant-based diet is also a contributing factor to long life as studies have shown. A second reason Kumi gave for Okinawan longevity is the weather. She explains: "There is nice weather most of the year. It can be hot in summer, but weather is good. Sunshine makes people happy. " As we have seen, MRS experts certainly would not disagree with Kumi's assessment.

PROFILE: Emi Toma

Emi is originally from mainland Japan but is married to an Okinawan. She is a loving and uber-dedicated mother to her son, Zen. Emi absolutely loves to learn. She wanted to practice speaking English, and I wanted to learn how to communicate better while I was in Okinawa, so we instantly bonded as friends.

Photo courtesy: Emi Toma
Emi and son, Zen, at his Nyugakushiki Ceremony on his first day of kindergarden

Emi married an Okinawan and relocated to the island from mainland Japan to live with him. She admitted to me that the transition to Okinawa took time, and her husband was instrumental in helping her successfully adjust to Okinawan life, which she explained can be *vastly different* from residing in mainland Japan. She relayed to me a story that I found interesting and one that MRS researchers corroborate. One of her challenges was getting accustomed to the Okinawans' practice of "Uchinanchu (Okinawan) Time."

This means that one should not be rushed or hurry time along. Mindfulness and living in the moment are the operative phrases here. This demands patience and an ability to just let the day unfold and transport you wherever. It requires that one must acquire the discipline to not hurry things along but let them occur in due time. With this mentality, delays are a way of life and to be expected.

Emi explained how this is so different from what she was accustomed to in mainland Japan. In one of our very enlightening conversation, she talked about being frustrated when she first relocated to Okinawa because, unlike in mainland Japan, where punctuality was absolutely the norm, it was the exact opposite in Okinawa.

Emi explained about having plans to meet with friends at a designated time and place. She discovered, however, on countless occasions in Okinawa, that when it came to being punctual for events, she was in the minority. Emi stated that people might show up hours later than the appointed time. She was also surprised that when they finally arrived at the event, there were virtually no apologies, and the other attendees did not appear to be bothered by their colleagues' late tendencies! When she expressed her frustration about this practice to her husband, he helped her better understand the cultural dynamics. His advice to Emi was that it was not a big deal for many if people were not on time.

He further noted that was just the way things were in Okinawa, and that people get to where they need to be whenever they are supposed to arrive at their destinations. This means that folks are not overly bothered by those who show up late. He explained that they may have gotten detoured by something else, so it is no problem. In other words, they will arrive at the designated event whenever they are supposed to get there. He also told her to not get stressed out about such things. His final pearls of wisdom were for her to spend more time understanding that she should just "go with the flow" rather than be bothered and stressed out by it. Emi heeded his advice, and from that point, was better be able to adjust to and enjoy the realities of life in Okinawa.

People who live longer tend to share the quality of being mindful and letting life unfold around them. Practicing mindfulness and not getting stressed by situations that cannot be controlled are tips practiced not just in Okinawa, but in other places where populations win at healthy aging. Not getting distracted and flustered by things beyond our control is an excellent practice for those of us interested in growing old and staying healthy.

Emi epitomizes *ichariba chode*

Like Kumi and Miss Phai, Emi also epitomizes *"Ichariba chode."* Emi and I became immediate friends and after leaving Okinawa, we have continued our friendship over the years via texts, phone calls and Facebook.

Photo by: MRAF
Emi Toma and MRAF in Okinawa

Emi's response to question about **why Okinawans are the oldest and healthiest people on earth** was: "Okinawan people think of each other. If they are angry with something or someone, they do not fight. No fighting. If something is wrong or if someone is upset, everybody counts One. Two. Three. Four. Five. Because the communities are ridiculously small, if we have problems or are fighting someone, maybe two weeks, three weeks, or one month later, we will run into each other. People help each other calm down."

I can't say enough fantastic things about Emi. If you go to the dictionary and look up words like kind, thoughtful, dedicated, and sincere, there should be a picture of her beside those definitions. Whenever I ask her a question about Okinawa, she's like a walking encyclopedia and goes above and beyond with her generosity of spirit and knowledge sharing. While I was staying at the Hotel Sunset Terrace we got into a lively conversation about why Okinawans live long and what they eat that keeps them so healthy. Emi mentioned a variety of foods and products. One that she particularly likes is a brown sugar called "kokuto." We ended our conversation and I left to go on a sightseeing tour.

Upon returning to my room late that evening, I was greeted with a huge basket of the foods she had mentioned, along with the note that explained what is kokuto. In the note, she said, "Locals have this like chocolate with jasmine tea or coffee. Brown sugar contains much better minerals than white sugar. I think that is one reasons for Okinawan's long life."

Emi was so right about kokuto. This brown sugar is manufactured in Okinawa and does possess many healthy longevity benefits. It is produced from sugar cane in a unique method that dates back to the seventeenth century. Grown in the ideal sunlit Okinawan environment near the ocean, it's chock-full of minerals provided by the ocean mist, including potassium, iron, and calcium.

I feel wonderfully blessed to know Emi and am certain that in the spirit of ichibara chode, we are family and friends for life!

PROFILE: Mr. Masakuni

I met Mr. Masakuni while casually strolling along the Sunabe Seawall in Chatan, Okinawa, not far from several military installations including Kadena Air Base, Camp Foster, and Camp Lester. People ranging from locals and military personnel to tourists from around the world hang out, jog, ride bikes, walk, and play along the seawall on the shores of the East China Sea. At night, it transforms into a robust and lively social scene. A variety of cafes, restaurants, and Japanese pubs known as izakayas provide fantastic opportunities to eat and socialize. Sunabe Seawall is known for its murals and super-colorful graffiti walls where artists showcase their amazing artwork on large stones and walls.

It is also known as the "epicenter for Okinawan surfing." Surfers love the area and describe the reef as like the area fronting Ala Moana Park in Oahu, Hawaii. The currents there are typically mild and make it a fantastic spot for scuba diving. Some people consider Okinawa and Hawaii as sister countries with similar climates and island vibes. Many Okinawans have relatives in Hawaii, which opened its doors to the Okinawan survivors of World War II. Hawaii allowed many Okinawans to rebuild their lives after the devastation and poverty they endured following the war.

I ran into Mr. Masakuni when I was on a mile-long walk along the Sunabee Seawall. My destination was the famous American Village and Ferris Wheel in the Mihama section of Chatan. I stopped momentarily to admire the breathtaking scenery around me—a combination of crystal-blue water, glistening sand, and brilliantly colored graffiti walls.

I plopped myself down on a ledge by the seawall, and, as I gazed out over the East China Sea, a perky older man by the name of Masakuni, who had his bicycle with him, also stopped to take a break. He asked me in an ultra-polite manner if he could talk to me and practice his English. I love to gab with others, and was more than willing to oblige, so we started a conversation.

During our chat, I told him that I had just started writing a book about Okinawa and why people there live so long. I asked if he would be willing to be interviewed and videotaped about why his people live so long. Without hesitation, he enthusiastically said, "Yes!" **Here are his insights about Okinawan longevity:**

"Okinawa beautiful. Weather very warm like Hawaii. People very friendly. Then, Okinawa very slow and laid back. Help people live longer. Living long. Tokyo very fast paced. Much different Okinawa. Okinawa slow. Laid back."

PROFILE: Takuya "Taku" Nakahashi

Taku is an international restauranteur. While originally from the Japanese mainland, he now makes Okinawa his home. He owns several successful businesses there, including Banana Fish and the Grill & Bistro Bar Garden in Chatan. Before relocating to Okinawa, he resided and had a restaurant in Australia and has lived around the world.

Taku is a very high-energy and ultra-personable business owner. He is married, and when I interviewed him, he and his beautiful wife were expecting their first child. I will forever remember his generosity as he hosted my first book reading at his popular Grill & Bistro Bar Garden.

Here is what Taku had to say about **why Okinawans are the oldest and healthiest people on earth:** "I believe that Okinawans live long lives because of the weather and that 80-90% of things people eat are grown here in their organic gardens. Farmers practice organic gardening. In their gardens, they do not use toxic chemicals. They believe in not using a lot of bad fertilizers on the veggies we feed the cows and pigs that we use for our beef and pork." Taku stressed that he uses prized Wagyu beef at his restaurants. This is a special beef that can be extremely expensive but offers a fantastic flavor.

Taku also felt that a huge reason why Okinawans enjoyed long, and healthy lives was because they are "at peace within themselves and others." He explained that "they don't tend to fight each other" and "are happy and almost always smiling."

As a restaurateur and bar owner, he made another interesting observation: "Some people do drink a lot, especially Awamori, which is a special sake that's only made here. They know how to enjoy drinking every day with family and friends." As we have learned, researchers have found that one of the principles that the longest-living people in the world follow is that they "take time to imbibe and unwind" with family, friends, and colleagues at the end of their day.

Taku also corroborated one more insight relative to what researchers have uncovered. He felt that because Okinawans practice a more relaxed approach to time, sometimes they are not on time, and that works to their advantage. Mindfulness and living in the moment are the operative terms here. This means that one must not hurry but let events occur in due time. He reiterated that with this mentality, delays are a way of life in Okinawa and should be expected.

PROFILE: Toshiyuki Ohno

Toshiyuki Ohno is owner of a chain of several successful beauty salons including Anan and Glam. When I interviewed him, his office was headquartered in mainland Japan. He was a frequent customer at Taku Nakahashi's Grill & Bistro Bar Garden restaurant. Taku introduced me to Mr. Ohno, who he had invited to my book reading at his restaurant. Mr. Ohno seemed genuinely excited to speak with me about his experiences in Okinawa and thoughts about healthy aging.

Mr. Ohno describes himself as someone who always stays active. He enjoys golf, softball, and adores karaoke. His friend Taku says that Mr. Ohno loves going to the many karaoke establishments in Okinawa and Japan. You may recall that one of MRAF's "8 Healthy Longevity Principles" is "Get in the groove and move," in other words, stay active attending a fun activity like karaoke.

Like many Japanese, Mr. Ohno has a work ethic that focuses on providing outstanding customer service. He talked about his need to always "Do something nice for the customers." My personal observation is that many Okinawans also subscribe to that sentiment and go out of their way to deliver incredible service to customers. The surprising thing for me is that they do this without any expectation of receiving a tip or additional compensation for such efforts. In fact, many of them seem to feel insulted when people try offering a tip! Someone explained to me that workers often feel that they should not expect to be paid extra by a customer just for doing their jobs.

Mr. Ohno also mentioned that the weather and clean environment in Okinawa contributed to people's longevity. He stated that "Okinawa is a small island, and the people have a nice heart. They are natural and give and take with each other. Everyone is a friend."

The last thing that he said was that he enjoyed going out drinking with his good friends. He smiled and stated that his wife of many years was understanding of his need to spend time with them, and he appreciated her for having that attitude. Like Mr. Ohno, the people who live the longest take time to cultivate friendships and support networks. Whether it is time spent drinking sake or singing a favorite song at a karaoke establishment, spending quality time with family and friends is a priority.

PROFILE: Noriko "Nina" Takiguchi

In the fall of 2017 and early winter of 2018, I was invited by Marisa Coleman and Derek Lumpkins of Northeastern University to teach three seminars based upon material from this book. At my last seminar in late January 2018, Noriko "Nina" Takiguchi attended my program. She had learned about it from another event she had attended where she met a best friend of mine, Monica Calzolari, who told Noriko about my workshop and invited her to come.

Noriko had been visiting Boston for a few months and would be returning soon to her home in Tokyo. She came to the seminar and we instantly bonded. She was staying one town over from where I lived and mentioned that she would be taking the subway home. I offered her a ride and we exchanged contact information. She told me that she had enjoyed the seminar and asked if I might speak with her again before she departed for Tokyo. We did get together for lunch, and I was struck by her thoughtfulness. She presented me with a gift she had made of two beautiful origami ornaments.

When we left our lunch, we promised to stay in touch. I told her that whenever I went back to Okinawa I would contact her because I usually stop in Tokyo. Little did I know that a month later, I would visit Okinawa. As promised, on my way back home, I contacted Noriko, who met me at Haneda Airport in Tokyo where we enjoyed lunch together.

Photo by: MRAF
Noriko Takiguchi and MRAF in Tokyo

Noriko had these observations as to **why Okinawans and Japanese live long and healthy lives.** She said: "The Okinawans have the ability to accept and embrace the present. Many people all over the world want to learn from the past, of course, but they might be asking for a quick fix. Sometimes it takes time. Japan has a long history of both good and bad, and maybe the Okinawans accept that very well."

It is so appropriate to end this section with Noriko's quote. In Part V, you will learn about how many Okinawans move on past life's challenges. That resiliency of spirit is a key ingredient in the healthy aging recipe.

Insights and perspectives from
Yeah... I Lived in Okinawa

In this next section, you will hear perspectives from American, international, and military people who have lived or are currently living in Okinawa. You will also be introduced to the 50,400 members (as of 06-21-21) of my beloved Okinawa cyberspace community who belong to the amazing Facebook group "Yeah...I Lived in Okinawa."

(https://www.facebook.com/groups/YeahILivedInOkinawa/about/)

I first learned about this amazing Facebook group from my cherished sensei (teacher) Vicki Cosper Wilson, who encouraged me to join this active international online group. She felt that I might benefit from hearing some of the different perspectives about Okinawa. She stressed that it was an opportunity to meet individuals who shared our adoration of the island. Vicki gave me an invaluable educational gift when she connected me to that powerful network.

The "About" section of the group says that it is: "For everyone who lived, lives, or wishes they lived in Okinawa and appreciates the culture and beauty of the island!" It is a site where those of us who have lived in Okinawa share our experiences and knowledge about a place we adore. My cyberspace family members range from millennials to people approaching centenarian status. We all have one thing in common: most of us cannot give enough accolades about the positive effect living in Okinawa has had on our lives.

I have been part of the gang only since 2017 and am thankful for its members welcoming me into their cyberspace kingdom and sharing their experiences of living in our Shangri-La. Many members have schooled me in the ways of Okinawans. Along with Vicki, two others have been particularly fantastic sensei (teachers) to me. These individuals are Donn Cuson and Rob Oechsle. Both gentlemen are avid Okinawan history buffs. They have made it their business to chronicle and preserve the history of Okinawa. Both have amassed an outstanding collection of rare and common photos that date back to WWII and before. I have been in awe of their seemingly limitless supply of vintage and current pictures of the island,

and the stories and commentary they made about them were amazing and so darn interesting.

I am profoundly grateful that Donn and Rob gave me permission to use some of their masterpieces in this book. You may recall that while I was in Okinawa for my first return visit, I made the decision to start writing this book. A quote attributed to Buddha and the Theosophists says, "When the student is ready, the teacher will appear."

That proverb rang true for me. When I was ready to learn more about Okinawa and returned there after 52 years, my teachers showed up in my life. It was not until adulthood that I discovered the ton of knowledge I had acquired about healthy aging principles while growing up in Okinawa. Those early lessons, however, were well ingrained inside my soul.

When I returned to Okinawa for the first time in 2016, I became a student who was ready to find teachers to school me on all things Okinawan. In the pages ahead, you will be introduced to two of my cherished teachers or, as the Okinawans say, sensei. My two top Okinawa sensei, Vicki Cosper Wilson, and Rob Oechsle will share their perspectives on healthy aging and living in Okinawa. I will begin by telling you about Vicki.

Photo courtesy MRAF
Left to right: Vicki Cosper Wilson, her sons Jackson and Jacob, MRAF, and Takeshi-Sensei, at Bank of Ryukyu Sanchin Recital in Naha, Okinawa.

PROFILE: Vicki Cosper Wilson

During the first trip to Okinawa after my 52-year hiatus, I met Vicki Cosper Wilson and her son Jacob by chance in the American Village section of Chatan. They were playing a game of Pokémon Go and looking for clues to their game. I was lost trying to locate an "authentic Okinawan restaurant" in the Mihama American Village shopping complex that someone had highly recommended. Not seeing anything that resembled such an establishment, I stopped them to ask for directions.

They immediately pointed to my destination, which was a mere few feet away. Duh! Before I resumed my journey, the three of us had a robust hour-long conversation in the parking lot. We became instant friends, which, as I have observed, seems to occur frequently in Okinawa. Our chat ended after we exchanged contact information and thus began my friendship with Vicki and her sons, Jacob, and Jackson. She would become one of my revered Okinawan sensei. Vicki contacted me after our chance encounter and extended an invitation to attend her son Jacob's sanshin recital at the Bank of the Ryukyu in Naha, Okinawa's capital city.

A sanshin is a popular traditional Okinawan instrument with a unique sound; some liken its shape to a banjo, but it sounds nothing like it. It has a long neck, three strings and is covered in snakeskin. Jacob, who speaks fluent Japanese, is an excellent sanshin player. He performs with a very seasoned group of Okinawan elders who respect this young man's ability. Vicki's youngest son, Jackson, is also an accomplished sanshin player.

Photo courtesy: Vicki Cosper
Jacob and Jackson Wilson at Sanshin recital with Takeshi-Sensei

To be a sanshin professional, you must achieve certain levels of proficiency. Her sons have done extremely well in obtaining these prized proficiencies. Jacob has achieved the respected level of Yuushuusho and his brother Jackson is Shinjinsho. This is a big deal. These prestigious titles are recognized by Okinawans every time Shimako-sensei announces them to audiences who are impressed by their high-level designations.

Vicki loves teaching and imparting knowledge to so many people. Not only is she home-schooling her youngest son, Jackson, but she also is a music teacher to children in Okinawa. Vicki's husband is a contractor for the military. They had lived in Okinawa for many years and after leaving it for another assignment, decided to return and do another tour of duty there because they loved living on the island.

On January 5, 2017, I brainstormed with Vicki about the title of this book. I mentioned that I had started writing and wanted to ask her opinion on the title. I told her I was thinking about calling it *Okinawa Is in Me*. Vicki, an American from Texas who is also an English and writing teacher, declared, "Why not call it, *The Okinawa in Me*?" As you can see, I took Vicki's sage advice.

Vicki and her sons have given me so many pointers about Okinawa, including things like:

- Understanding life on Kadena Air Base
- Where to find great shopping places from Daiso (a popular and fabulous dollar store) to the famous Kokusai Street in Naha
- Great restaurants like Sam's Anchor and other local Okinawan establishments
- How to eat taco rice and Blue Seal beni imo (purple sweet potato) ice cream
- The "Yeah… I Lived in Okinawa" Facebook group
- Okinawan efficiency cars and license plates
- Sanshin and other Okinawan music

Vicki offered some interesting insights about Okinawan longevity. She said that Okinawans "know how to have fun." She went on to relay an experience where her sons played for Takeshi-Sensei's (the gentleman who is her son's official teacher) village meeting. "The boys played for Takeshi-Sensei's village Sunday meeting/party. What a treat! Japanese people know how to have fun! After the meeting, we ate Okinawan food and then the boys joined some others to perform. We had a sort of white elephant gift exchange where a typical gift is boxes of tissues. Then the karaoke began. This is a popular pastime and hobby here. Takeshi-Sensei's wife goes every Monday. Many of my local friends go often as well. You probably saw all the karaoke places when you were here."

She continued: "Another thing you might enjoy knowing is at the New Year Dinner, the elder serves sake or juice to each person. I interpret it as a sort of blessing. The name of it is Otoso. My boys have experienced this with Shimako-Sensei's father this year and father-in-law in the past."

I am forever indebted to Vicki and her family for the numerous things they have taught me as I have navigated my way through Okinawan culture.

Wondering what it is like to reside in Okinawa? If you think I am uber-excited about having lived there, you will see that I have plenty of company. To illustrate my point, below is a series of posts that I made on "Yeah… I

Lived in Okinawa." The first one was posted upon returning to Okinawa after my 52-year hiatus.

YEAH… I Lived in OKINAWA Facebook post about:

What it was like to return to Okinawa after 52 years

Posted on Facebook on February 4, 2017

Martha R.A. Fields

I left Kadena AFB in 1964 and for the 2017 New Year returned to Okinawa after 52 years. This was a dream come true and I had such a spectacular time that I am writing a book about Okinawa in ME. If you have any pictures you can send via this post from the period 1960-1964 of Okinawa and/or Kadena AFB that you would be willing for me to put in my book, I would be very appreciative! I would also love it if you would reply to this post and provide any quotes about your thoughts on living in Okinawa and/or why you think Okinawan people live long and healthy lives based upon your experience there. Please know that I will be publishing your quotes in my book and that by responding to this post, you are allowing me to do so.

Russell Goutierez: Love it! We arrived there in 1964. Maybe we passed each other at the airport. LOL

Martha RA Fields: That is quite possible.

Dee Denille Clark Demyan: Did you go solo or with a group? I was there in Oct/Nov with a group of Kubasaki friends. It had been 46 years for me since I'd left. Trip was a big bucket list item…. And one fantastic trip!

Martha RA Fields: I went solo but got to meet so many awesome people.

Matilda Robinson: I was there with my husband and kids 2008 - 2011. Not a day goes by that I don't long to be there - I will always miss Okinawa and the incredible people I knew. It was like magic.

Ken Hill: I taught English at Nago English School for eight months. When I got off duty, I would get into my civies and take the bus up from Onna Point where I was stationed. That was the highlight of my tour. I wondered how long that school remained. I was teaching to Okinawa students English only, mostly pronunciation and conversation. It was an old wooden school in Nago with about four Okinawa teachers and a principal. I don't know anybody at Kadena, I was about 20 miles north.

Suzanne Jane Patton: I taught ESL at a middle school near Koza complete with English books from England. It led to many funny misunderstandings. The book introduce words of a slightly more sophisticated language. Since the introduction explained it was written for Adult ESL classes.

Lisa Ammons: Did it bother you that nothing was like you remembered?

Martha RA Fields: I did see something that had not basically changed since when I left in 1964. Kadena Elementary building did not change. When I saw it, I knew exactly where I was standing. There was a mural on the wall that was new.

Suzanne Jane Patton: I lived across the street from the school in 64. Our house had a white telephone pole laying along the flower bed. Long story about that pole. Brought it with us from Kadena Circle.

Anne Freimuth Statland: What a wonderful trip for you! We were there in Nov/Dec and I am ready to go back NOW!

Martha RA Fields: I am also ready to return and soak in more knowledge about this mystical and magical place!

Second Facebook post on: August 10, 2017

Martha RA Fields
· August 10, 2017 · Melrose

WOULD YOU LIKE TO BE QUOTED IN MY BOOK?
It is titled: *THE OKINAWA in ME: FINALLY Finding MY IKIGAI (Reason for Being!)*

I am looking for other people who are willing to be quoted or want to share their perspectives and stories about living in Okinawa and these topics.

Please submit anything you would like for me to consider including in my book by August 31st as my deadline for completing the book is rapidly approaching.

Here are some of the comments that I received:

Ashley Benefield: I just returned to the United States 3.5 weeks ago. I lived there for 3 years with my family. Living there completely turned my life around. And it's really an honor to even be considered on your book project. Everyone should know about the magic and beauty of this island. I think this is amazing.

Donn Cuson: I have around 4,000 photos, etc. on my Okinawa history website that date from 1945 to 1972, if there is anything you see that you would like to use contact me and I can provide high res scans www. rememberingokinawa.comManageRemembering Okinawa - 1945 to 1972 United…rememberingokinawa.com

Margy English Metzler: "I lived on Okinawa for seven years (2004-2011) and by far our best duty station. The Okinawa and Japanese people were wonderful and so welcoming. So, don't believe all you read in the newspapers. I just went back April 2017 for a visit, and it was as wonderful and beautiful as I Remembered."

Km Clark Elliott: It was a magical time for so many for sure. I for one remember our 4 years there as the best years of my life. Ever since we left, the only place on earth that I would want to go to again.

Tom Nugen: I Believe The Okinawan Folk Loooove to Have Fun in Many Aspects of their lives, Its Contagious as you can see. Kubasaki Senior (74) Tom Nugen enjoying a photo op at Hajaeme Ichis Yamaha shop, Naha, Okinawa, circa 1974.

Martha RA Fields: I love the picture and the quote is great. Thanks, Tom for contributing to my book 😎 😊.

Donna Dernbach Aponte: I lived on Oki for 15 years. All my children were born there, and I was on the first American Haari team (all female too) to compete in the small local races.

"I am not Okinawan by blood, but Oki in spirit and heart." 🖤❤️

Martha RA Fields: Wow, Donna, that's how I feel. You said it SO well!

James Cummings: Hi Martha, I lived on Okinawa for 20 years, and still go back once a year to visit my wife's family. I was there for the first International Conference on Longevity in 2000.

Scott Storch: Orion [a beer popular in Okinawa], awamori [a sake made in Okinawa] and Marlboros the real Okinawan secret to longevity!

Sharon Gima: My Okinawan husband has made sure we established a close relationship with the Hormel Company. Long live Spam!!

Terry Kile: Hello Martha...I lived in Okinawa from 1960-1962. First in Kadena Circle off base and then on Kadena AFB.

Matilda Robinson: I lived in Yomitan from Aug. 2008 - June 2011. I think of that sweet island and my incredible life there every single day. Okinawans are the kindest and friendliest people I have ever met.

Third Facebook post: February 24, 2018

Martha RA Fields

Hi Everyone. Greetings from Okinawa! I arrived in Okinawa last night and am thrilled to be back. I am trying to get feedback from people on what I have written in my upcoming book about why people in Okinawa live so long and why many of us who have lived there were impacted in a positive way by living there.

Also, if you have any comments/quotes that I can put in about why Okinawans are the oldest and healthiest people in the world, I would appreciate you responding to this post. Please know that by sending your post that you give me permission to print what you said in my upcoming book about Okinawa.

All the best,
Martha

Here are some responses to my post.

Debbie Birdsall Kolkmeier: They say it's the coral calcium.

Kennesu O Weir: Martha, Mom on Okinawa told me she gave up red meat over 20 years ago since returning from the States in '84. In March she'll be 88; loves her Goya, Other Okinawan vegetables, no Coca Cola, White polished rice a few times a month & fish is part of her diet. Mom has an active mind & walks on her own two feet.

Bill Bechtel: genetics

Ashley Benefield: There is an excellent documentary on Amazon Prime called Okinawa. It goes into detail why their culture is ideal. While I'm certain it's partly genetics, I also believe level of stress, quality of life, quality of food (non-processed), and purpose have a huge impact. I certainly felt a huge change in my quality of life while I lived there, in a very positive way.

I absolutely agree with you. There's no denying that there's something more going on there, something better. I know this because I felt it. That's all the proof I need. I look forward to reading your finished product 😊 🙂.

Debbie Kawamoto: The way they eat, always show thanks and appreciation for what they have in life, work hard but play hard too, make music and dance apart of their life, don't stress over the little stuff and take life a day at a time.

My mother was Okinawan, and I grew up there until I was 17, what I wrote above, is my observation of my mom and my relatives and the people in general.

Gerwlyn Aharen: I can also agree with this. The older Okinawan's have so many wonderful stories to tell. Some are heartbreaking about loved ones lost in the war. They are also very strong and committed to family.

Phai Brackett: "I believe it's mostly because of what is inside of the Okinawa people's hearts and minds. Their heart is so beautifully, pure, and kind, and they are MINDFUL OF HOW THEIR ACTIONS AFFECT OTHERS. It shows in everything they say and do. Oh, how I love Okinawa and its people 💕 🤍 🌸 🏵️."

Donald Kempton: Isolated islanders with a slow lifestyle pace along with smaller stature and healthy food. All a recipe for longevity. It's why we tall angry fat guys die at 50 😄

Ann Parey: A more interesting study would be why the death age is slowly declining. Many studies have been focused on the advanced age of the Okinawans, but none have addressed recent research findings that indicate the death rate is declining. Why? That would be valuable research.

Kim Roe: Because they are becoming too much like Americans. They have more of our fast food places on Okinawa now.

Ann Parey: I arrived on Okinawa in 1968. The island has changed from remote to modernized. Compare it to the death rate of other outer islands that have remained the same. That would be valuable.

Mary Chalk: According to last weeks' Time magazine, it is a lifetime of support by the same group of people. There is always someone to depend on.

Diane Downey Brennan: Another factor is respect for elders. Our society often prefers to put our elders in places when they can't live alone anymore. We also don't listen to our elders' stories.

Donald Kempton: I was just talking to a coworker about this. She had to put her mother into assisted living because of Alzheimer's. She was surprised at how few families come to visit their elders. (This is in Okinawa). Sadly, things are changing and not necessarily for the better.

Cynthia Wallace Kleppang: Martha, also consider the documentary called Happy on Netflix or Amazon. It's about the science of happiness, and it touches on longevity and happiness in Okinawa. Also, look for the extras on YouTube that covers even more. Lucky to be there!!!

Martha RA Fields: Thanks so much, Cynthia for the information!

Charles Patten: Okinawa is one of the five blue zones in the world for longer living.

Martha RA Fields: Yes. I am talking about the Blue Zones and Dan Buettner's research on them in my upcoming book. Am really surprised that most people don't know about them!
Kim Roe: I believe their family values. Generations of families all live in the same house. Their work habits (and their exercise regime at work) and the way they work hard but also play hard. They drink Awamori [a sake made in Okinawa] and eat Miso soup. We were there for 6 years and loved it. Our 2 sons grew up there and they loved it!!! Life was simple, no keeping up with the Jones's like in America.

Martha RA Fields: Fantastic insights. I spoke with someone yesterday in Okinawa who also said that Awamori is a key ingredient to Okinawan Longevity! 😎😊.

Kim Roe: Yes, you may. I only wish we had the money in our budget to some day visit Okinawa again. I have a young cousin who is there with her hubby now.

Okinawa Man: I grew up in Okinawa from 1957 to 1970. It was island living. Pretty laid back. People were nice despite the discrimination by the Americans and the Japanese mainlanders. The lower half of the island was just as pristine as the northern end is now.

Roz Avery Fuller: I raised my two children on Okinawa while teaching and counseling at Kadena HS. We all consider it our home and yearn for it every day. I can hardly wait to read your book. Thank you so much for writing it.

Summing up: What it is like to live in Okinawa

I have become lifelong friends with a number of people in this Facebook group. As you can see, living in Okinawa was a transformative and positive experience for many of us. Visit the "YEAH…I Lived in Okinawa" Facebook page to learn more about the insights of those who have experienced life in the place were people live the longest and are the healthiest on the planet.

In the next chapter, you'll hear directly from my sensei, Rob Oechsle, an American who has lived in Okinawa for over 45 years. You will also discover some secrets of *moving from tragedy to triumph and gloom to glee.*

CHAPTER 9:

Moving from Tragedy to Triumph and Gloom to Glee

In the previous chapter, you saw how many people verified what international medical and scientific experts have confirmed via their rigorous, meticulous, peer-reviewed, and evidence-based studies. It can be verified that Okinawans win the Olympic gold medal for healthy aging.

As mentioned previously, many Okinawans, especially as they grow old, take on the role of sensei (teacher). Senseis abound, even overflow, in Okinawa. People who practice karate (which was developed in the old Ryukyu Kingdom on Okinawa) are undoubtedly aware of this powerful term. In Okinawa, the role of teacher is highly revered and almost sacred. Members of Okinawan society view it to be of the highest human order to have the honor and opportunity to share and impart information they know to help others to grow via their watchful tutelage. Below is a profile of my Okinawan American sensei, Rob Oechsle.

Photo by MRAF
MRAF and her American/Okinawan Sensei (Teacher) Rob
Oechsle at Ryukyu Mura, Yomitan, Okinawa

PROFILE: Rob Oechsle

Rob Oechsle is an Okinawan historian par excellence and my sensei. Rob was stationed in Okinawa during the last years of the Vietnam War. His tour of duty was at an Army Base called Camp Kue (currently Camp Lester), which is not far from my old home at Kadena Air Base. He served as a pharmacy technician at the base hospital and has lived in Okinawa for over 45 years. Some jokingly say that although Rob was born in the US, his love for the island and his relentless mission to chronicle Okinawa's past and current history makes him more Okinawan than some indigenous Okinawans.

Rob is married to the beautiful Etsuko. Their love for each other permeates a room. After meeting her, I totally understood why he chose to stay with her in Okinawa rather than move back to the United States. Rob and Etsuko's union (of over 40 years) produced three daughters.

Rob is a spectacular photographer and Okinawan history expert. He showcases his extensive body of photographic and historical perspectives about Okinawa on Flickr and goes by the name of Okinawa Soba (Rob). Many of his amazing photos, like those featured in this book, are simply breathtaking. If you are interested in seeing more of his spellbinding photos, as well as his historical and contemporary writings about the island, go to:

https://www.flickr.com/photos/okinawa-soba/albums

My first time meeting Rob Oechsle

While Rob and I had communicated via our Facebook group, "Yeah… I Lived in Okinawa," we had never formally met in person. He frequently makes amazing posts there and I am constantly replying with kudos to his colorful pictures, historical information, and humor-laced insights about the island. Because we are both active members on this powerful site, I did not think of him as a stranger, but more as a trusted friend and colleague.

I had reached out to Rob and texted him in advance of my trip to Okinawa in February 2018. I asked if he could meet with me in person while I was there, so I could gain some of his vast wisdom about the island. In addition, I let him know that I had two pressing questions that had caused me to catch a serious case of writer's block. Despite everything I tried, I just could not work through it. Since I was on the last leg of my book-writing journey, I had to address it and finish my book. What was the cause of my writer's block? I needed to write about an issue related to Okinawa that had confounded me. An interesting dynamic I have witnessed is that many Okinawan people have told me that:

"Okinawans do not get stressed!"

After I kept hearing that statement repeated almost verbatim by so many people I met from all walks of Okinawan life, the researcher and writer in me had to probe further and explore exactly what they meant by that statement, because doesn't everybody experience stress? I genuinely wanted to know why they felt that way. I decided that when I heard people make that declaration, I would follow up and in a probing tone say, "I know you've said that Okinawans don't experience stress, but is that *really* true?"

This is no exaggeration. You might expect people to walk back such a statement when pressed: "Oh, well of course everyone lives with at least SOME stress..." But no. Almost every time I probed; they only became more adamant. It became clear at that point in the conversation that they wanted to drill into my head that yes, they believed that "Okinawans do not get stressed!"

Something else I observed when I interviewed Okinawans and Japanese is that they absolutely confirmed what experts have spent billions of dollars and years of research time to prove: stress does not dominate the lives of many Okinawan people. Once I realized that indeed the peer-reviewed evidence and perceptions by Okinawans were in sync, I had to dig deeper and uncover why Okinawans feel non-stressed. What are their secrets to a stress-free life?

I harbored another Okinawan stress-related question that I wanted answered to get past my writer's block. It was: "How could older Okinawans and their children who lived through the utter atrocities of WWII go through that experience and not feel stressed?"

The violence that took place in Okinawa during WWII cannot be understated. I mentioned previously that during the battle of Okinawa, which lasted only a little over two months (April 1 to June 22, 1945,) it is estimated that close to 200,000 people lost their lives on this tiny island.

Surely the people who lived through those trying times and their children had to suffer some type of PTSD-like symptoms or other residual mental ailments caused by that war? Bad things do happen -- typhoons, tsunamis, and pandemics -- that must stress out even those who excel at "destressing from stress." People in Okinawa who are currently 100 or 110 would have gone through not only the COVID-19 pandemic, but they would have also survived the 1918 deadly Spanish Flu Pandemic along with tons of other stress-bearing historical events not the least was WWI and WWII.

Considering all the tragic atrocities that Okinawans (especially the elder ones) had endured, how were they able to successfully bounce back and declare that they do not get stressed? I could not understand how a group of people who had withstood unthinkable things (such as surviving during the WWII Battle of Okinawa by eating cockroaches in dark caves in the jungle surrounded by venomous habu snakes) could be so well-adjusted. Where others would have perished, the Okinawans came out of the WWII nightmare and rebuilt their lives. They eventually flourished and for generations have won the coveted title of the world's most healthy and longest-living people. How DID they do it, I asked myself over and over.

Exactly why Okinawans felt they had no stress

I did a lot of soul-searching about exactly who in Okinawa could break down this "we have no stress here" attitude. It did not take long to come up with an answer. I knew the person who could provide me with answers was my dear American/Okinawan sensei, Rob Oechsle. Not only would Rob be of great help, but so would his incredible wife, Etsuko. Here is what they told me about the Okinawan secrets to healthy aging by not getting stressed.

Rob told me that he had to do one thing to illustrate the amazing resilience of the Okinawan people and how they cope with stress. While I was in Okinawa in February 2018, he would take me to two caves in the jungle. The caves were in a township called Yomitan, not too far from where I was staying in Chatan.

I love jungles and rain forests and have visited a number in my lifetime, including the amazing Amazon jungle in Iquitos, Peru and in Tikal, Guatemala. Nevertheless, I was not 100% sure if I was ready for Rob's proposed Indiana-Jones-like adventure into these caves in the jungles of Okinawa. On February 27, I met Rob Oechsle for the first time in person. Our rendezvous location was a popular meeting point in the Mihama American Village area of downtown Chatan. It is a trendy retail, amusement, shopping, and entertainment indoor and outdoor mecca that was built to resemble what the designers felt represented a typical American city. To me, it felt like a combination open-air and indoor mall that I might visit in California or Florida.

I would meet Rob near the famous Mihama Ferris Wheel and the multiplex theater. The blockbuster movie *Black Panther* had just played to audiences at the high-tech movie theater at this mall. There were gigantic *Black Panther* billboards near the theater entrance. Several Okinawans told me that the movie was so popular that people stood in a mile-long line to see it. The billboards for this action thriller were so colorful and impressive that I could not help but stop and take a few pictures.

I was ecstatic to finally meet the Rob Oechsle whose photos and posts I had enjoyed so much on our "Yeah… I Lived in Okinawa" Facebook group. Since we are both talkers, we spoke almost nonstop from the moment I laid eyes on him at 2 p.m. until I returned to my Airbnb apartment around 9 in the evening.

I smiled, then pinched myself while thinking about what a great opportunity it was to be in Okinawa, the place where I had learned how to love learning. I had received so much knowledge from my incredible Doris Day-look-alike fifth grade schoolteacher, Miss O'Brien, in the 1960s. Now, I was continuing my knowledge journey over a half-century later under the tutelage of the one and only Rob Oechsle. I told him about my writer's block and that I was hoping he could help me get out of neutral and solve what was ailing me.

Rob immediately responded to my request by saying that of course he could help me out. To do so, we had to do one thing first. "What's that?" I asked.

He replied, "I'm taking you to the jungle and the caves in Yomitan! Are you game?"

I replied, "Absolutely, just call me Indiana Jones Martha Fields. And, by the way, I love jungles and rainforests. I've been to some real nice ones, especially in Jamaica and in Peru." We both laughed loudly, then piled into his car and our journey began to see the "Dead End and Happy Caves" in Yomitan, Okinawa.

En route to the jungle and caves

Before hitting the jungle and the two caves, I had just one request of Rob. I wanted to stop by another place in Yomitan called Ryukyu Mura. It is a theme park that was built to replicate an ancient Okinawan village from the Ryukyu Kingdom. This is a must-see and guaranteed good-time destination and escape back in time. I had visited there on my first trip back to Okinawa and taken a portrait in a traditional Okinawan outfit. The picture I had taken just over a year before showed me with about 40 additional pounds. I wanted to get another taken at my new size and was hoping to use it in my book. Rob agreed to make that detour.

January 2017-Picture of MRAF taken at Ryukyu Mura

Once we reached our destination and exited the car, I started to lock my car door. Rob quickly said, "Oh, you don't have to do that. Everything is safe here. No one bothers to lock up their car or their homes. People will not try to get in and steal anything. We just don't do that here!"

"Okay…" I said, while thinking, "*Wow, this truly IS Shangri-La.*" On countless occasions, I had witnessed how honest Okinawans are by nature. I have also heard stories where people have accidentally left behind their pocketbooks or wallets filled with money. No worries, this is Okinawa. When they were recovered, nothing had been stolen or tampered with by anyone. I would love to see that behavior copied in the USA.

With the portrait field trip to Ryukyu Mura out of the way, we set out to see "The Caves" in the jungle of Yomitan, Okinawa.

The Battle of Okinawa and the atrocities of WWII

I want to set the stage with a bit of history about what happened to Okinawan citizens inside those caves and villages during World War II. I have mentioned several times the importance of Okinawa's ideal and strategic location in Far East Asia. Historical accounts abound of countries that have viewed it as something akin to a crown jewel. For thousands of years, foreign entities have invaded this "Keystone of the Pacific" in a quest to conquer and own a piece of this invaluable real estate. You may recall that the ancient Chinese, some 2,500 years ago, sent out expeditions whose mission was to find and capture this prized land that they called the "Land of the Immortals."

Do not forget that karate was invented in Okinawa. After all, these peace-loving people had to find a way to defend themselves from incursions by neighbors from Mainland Japan, China, North Korea, Taiwan, Russia, India, and Vietnam. The Asia-Pacific segment of World War II began after a surprise and deadly attack on Pearl Harbor in Hawaii and an invasion on the Malay Peninsula in 1941. What you may not know is that:

> *During World War II, the largest amphibious warfare attack in the Pacific Theater took place in Okinawa, Japan.*

Rob gave me a copy of an outstanding book, *Himeyuri Peace Museum: The Guidebook.* I highly recommend reading it. It provides some fascinating and gripping firsthand stories from Okinawans who survived the ravages of WWII. The book notes that in April 1945, the US forces began landing on Okinawa Island (540,000 soldiers, reserve troops, and personnel). The Japanese had a much smaller force, made up of about 110,000 men.

According to the *Guidebook*, "These Japanese troops avoided combat at the point where U.S. forces landed and took positions underground, taking advantage of natural caves found here and there in the hills of the Southern Okinawa island. They made the Battle of Okinawa as a war of attrition; they kept the U.S. troops occupied in Okinawa and tried to delay the landing of U.S. troops on Japanese soil. This strategy resulted in more casualties among the Okinawan people and extended battle for another 90 days. This meant that Okinawa was exploited to preserve the imperial national polity. In other words, Okinawa was abandoned like a piece of stone, a worthless object."[64]

> *According to the Himeyuri Peace Museum, close to 200,000 people were murdered in Okinawa in just 90 days from April 1 to June 22, 1945. Other estimates place the number of war dead closer to 250,000 individuals.*

Included in the number of war dead were:

- Okinawans (military, non-military participants and civilians)
- Mainland Japanese soldiers
- Individuals fighting for the USA

The magnitude of these numbers cannot be dismissed. After all, it is a tiny island, only about 70 miles long and 7 miles across. These enormous casualties for such a small but strategic place included innocent Okinawan women and children along with their teachers and parents. Okinawan people endured deplorable and unimaginable war conditions. They were subjected to such inhumane treatment such as:

- Being used as human shields and killed.
- Whole families and schoolteachers along with their students were forced by the Japanese military to commit suicide rather than

---

[64] Yoshiko Shimabukuro, *Himeyuri Peace Museum: The Guidebook* (Okinawa, Japan: October 2016), 2.

subsist in a war-torn society where dying was considered a better option than living.

- Surviving on meager meals consisting of cockroaches, rainwater, and, on a good day, a staple diet of purple sweet potatoes, a few kernels of rice and wild foods and berries.

Many had to leave their homes and hide in caves deep inside jungles infested with highly venomous habu snakes. Others sought refuge in the mountains. At this point, you might ask some questions that I often pondered. They are:

- Despite the unthinkable hardships Okinawans suffered, how did they manage to bounce back after WWII to become the oldest and healthiest living people on earth? Why was it possible for them to accomplish that feat?
- How can I learn from the Okinawans about their secrets for moving from tragedy to triumph and gloom to glee?
- Most importantly, how can I apply this wisdom to my life when I hit tragic and tough times?

In the pages ahead, you will receive the answer to these questions. To begin understanding this dynamic, we will return to the tour of the two caves that Rob took me to visit.

Experiencing the carnage of WWII by visiting the Yomitan caves

To help me comprehend what life was like for some Okinawans during WWII, on Tuesday afternoon, February 27, 2018, my Okinawan sensei Rob Oechsle took me on the adventure of a lifetime through the jungles of Okinawa to visit the infamous "Dead End/Sad Cave" and the "Happy Cave" in Yomitan. We were near the beaches where the April 1, 1945, invasion of the island began and was followed by some of the bloodiest battles fought during WWII.

The first cave we visited is known to many foreigners as the "Sad Cave." Okinawans call it "Chibi Chiri Gama," which means "The Dead End Cave." Rob told me that the word "gama" means "cave." It is from the ancient dialect of Okinawa, the Uchinaaguchi language. Despite the bright, perfectly sunny day, I immediately felt a dark, dank heaviness come over me as I stepped out of Rob's car onto the holy and sacred soil of this location.

The first words from Rob, my Indiana-Jones-type tour guide, were about safety. He pointed to a colorful sign bearing an image of a coiled snake. "Let's just remember that we're in a jungle and habu are present. Make sure you watch where you step!" Rob did not have to explain what is a habu. Anyone who has lived in Okinawa is aware that the habu is part of a venomous snake family whose relatives include rattlesnakes and cobras, and whose bite could leave the victim permanently disabled or even dead! I am petrified of snakes, so my guard was immediately up. Despite my snake phobia, I was determined to enter and explore this cave and shrine with Rob.

Photo by: Rob Oechsle
Check out the deadly habu snake sign adorning
the entrance to the "Dead End Cave"

Our trek began by descending a long set of stairs surrounded by the thick tropical brush of the jungle. Walking down into the cave area felt like we were descending into some type of hell. Carefully navigating the steep concrete steps to the entrance of the cave site, I had to pause and take in the scenery and sights of this big shrine, draped in colorful cloth streamers that floated in the steamy air at the mouth of the cave. I also noticed this enormous tree and had to take a picture of it.

I continued to be haunted by this site as I peered into the darkness of a massive cave. Beside the cave entrance was a large memorial, at the top of which sat a looming statue of a man strumming a sanshin. Surrounding this figure were sculptures of skeletons and very sorrow-filled ghost-like faces that seemed to be crying out. More of these figures were also hidden inside the cave-like base of the memorial. They appeared to be spirit faces of mothers holding babies and images of adult, baby, and child-like faces. These pictures depicted people writhing in pain and suffering.

Photo by: MRAF
Man playing sanshin and surrounded by haunting skeleton carvings inside cave

Rob told me that the sign I saw warned people not to walk any further to enter the cave. Because this is considered a sacred graveyard and holy ground, we could peer into it but were not allowed to walk inside. Brightly colored cloth streamers were draped in front.

Photo by: MRAF
Rob Oechsle at Dead End Cave, Yomitan, Okinawa

I did not know the story of the Dead End Cave. I had never heard about it either. Like the seasoned and wise tour guide that he is, Rob explained the significance of the cave by telling me the story of "Chibi Chiri Gama." Here is that tale:

"Chibi Chiri Gama" (The Dead End Cave)

As the WWII Battle of Okinawa descended upon Yomitan in central Okinawa, many residents were forced to flee and hide in dark caves like the Dead End Cave. Villagers sought refuge there rather than risk getting captured by the Imperial Japanese Army on one side or the United States, along with a few Allied troops, on the other.

I was haunted by this eerie and grotesque history as I peered into the darkness of the caves and imagined the hell that people would have experienced. Rob mentioned that 140 people from the village took refuge in this cave, believing that the natural shelter might possibly protect them from the air raids overhead and the shelling from ships offshore.

Conditions inside the cave were horrendous and individuals had few comforts of life. The caves were dark and damp with no sunlight. The villagers had little food except cockroaches, wild berries, plants and perhaps occasionally a taste of a luxury item like a small ball of rice or Beni imo (purple sweet potatoes.) Some accounts offer graphic details, describing an overwhelming reek of feces, urine, death, and decay.

However, the initial invasion met little resistance, because most of the Japanese troops had moved south to prepare a more deadly "welcome" for the invading Americans. Sadly, it was the innocent civilians at Chibi Chiri Gama who became the most famous casualties of those first hours of the long Battle of Okinawa. Beginning with Chibi Chiri Gama, over the weeks and months of fighting, thousands of Okinawans would gradually witness the unbelievable atrocities that so often accompany the violent conflicts of war.

I imagined what it must have been like for the Okinawan people. They were homeless, and the cave was their refuge because they had had nowhere else to go. I also thought about how so many of them probably felt their world was coming to an end. Some had to feel hopeless and doubted if they would ever find a way out of the darkness. Okinawan civilians had also been subject to psychological warfare carried out by the Imperial Japanese Army. They were told that if captured by American troops, their situation would become even more dire.

The US soldiers were painted by the Imperial Japanese Army to be barbarians who would rape, kill, mutilate, and even eat the Okinawans if captured. Okinawan eyewitness accounts say that the Japanese soldiers gave the civilian villagers who went to hide in the cave poison and hand grenades to commit suicide should they fall into hands of US soldiers. It was stressed that committing suicide (shudan jiketsu) was a far more honorable way to die than being tortured by the Americans.

As predicted, the American troops did discover the cave dwellers in the hours post invasion. Sadly, out of the 140 people, a total of 84 people lost their lives. Some of the casualties fought back with crude bamboo spears. Others committed suicide by using the poison and grenades they had been given by Japanese soldiers. Several people used knives and sharp farming tools to slit the throats of their children and/or other family members to avoid captivity and dishonor.

As I stood on the sacred grounds of Chibi Chiri Gama, I felt the spirits of those men, women, and children who had lost their lives in those dark, dank caves lingering around us. I was moved to tears and sorrow encompassed my heart as I tried to imagine the unimaginable. How did whole families and teachers with their students commit suicide together in that place?

Photo by: MRAF
I was moved to tears at this sacred WWII site

I felt the magnitude and intensity of the decision they had to make before ending their lives and, in some cases, the lives of their beloved family members. Imagine the head games they must have been played before those victims drifted onto death's door? They must have surmised that it was not worth staying alive and subjecting themselves to a life of "hell on earth." Many may have decided that staying on earth was too painful and chose death, which they felt was the lesser of the two evils they had confronted!

The villagers had all experienced things that no one should have to witness. They could not escape the stench of death nor the uncertainty of whether they would be among the living at the conclusion of the war.

Several Okinawans I talked to had known people who perished in the war. Some knew children and schoolteachers who had committed mass suicide. Stories abound about how these kids and their esteemed sensei jumped to their deaths from steep cliffs rather than continue wallowing in the hell that they were experiencing on earth. To learn more about this dark moment in Okinawan history, you may wish to read the incredible page-turner of a book I have previously referenced: *Himeyuri Peace Museum: The Guidebook.*

Something caught my eye as Rob, and I continued our tour at Chibi Chiri Gama. It was a giant monument that had letters etched deeply into the slabs of the memorial wall. Rob continued to weave his haunting tale. He said that the writing on this huge tablet documented exactly who died and to which families they had belonged. I moved closer to the structure and had to take the picture below, because it really tugged at my soul and heartstrings.

Rob said that the lettering first noted the family name of the individuals who had been killed. The succeeding names, which were written in Japanese, were the actual names and ages of each family member who perished in the cave. In building this amazing monument, the Okinawans wanted each person who died to be remembered.

Photo by: MRAF
Cave family death roll call

For example, in the picture above, the family included: An elder who was 54 years old, followed by his spouse, 48, and all their relatives whose ages were 15, 11, 9, 7, and 5 years old. All these people were either murdered or committed suicide. How utterly tragic!

For what seemed like an eternity, I stood numb and motionless, clasping my hands in a prayerful gesture to the heavens. The sadness that consumed me was so intense that tears streamed down my face and my body trembled. To add more fuel to my sorrow, Rob provided insights into the politics of how some vocal modern right-wing nationalists, primarily from mainland Japan, operate under a "conspiracy-theory mode."

They proclaim that the inhumane atrocities at the Dead End Cave and in WWII during the Battle of Okinawa never happened. Those who tout these bizarre theories seem to genuinely believe that the cave stories were fabricated. These nonbelievers have made it their business to travel to the cave and have attempted (once successfully) to destroy parts of this sacred shrine.

Other Japanese right-wing nationalists also look down on the Okinawans who regret what happened to them in the war, saying they should have been proud to die and commit suicide for the Emperor and the nation of Japan. The people who not only know that it did happen, and in some cases lived through those days, have likewise made it their business to repair and rebuild damage caused by history deniers. These Okinawans continue their peaceful mission to never see human destruction of the type witnessed in war-torn Okinawa or the nuclear destruction at Nagasaki and Hiroshima ever again!

I learned an amazing fact: some believe that more people perished in the war waged on Okinawa than did in the nuclear bombings in Japan. I did, however, feel a little comforted and saw a ray of positivity shine when Rob said that the monuments and colorful pieces of cloth hanging from the entrance to the cave were placed there by peace-loving Okinawans and mainland Japanese who were adamant about letting the world know what took place at that cave in Yomitan.

They want to do everything in their power to prevent another war or atrocities like those committed there to ever happen again – not just in Okinawa, but around the world.

I also noticed some bottles of water placed as offerings at the entrance to the cave. Some believe that those who have passed on get thirsty traveling around in the afterworld and that the water is there to help them quench their thirst.

Many tragically lost their precious lives in that cave. It became the dead end to their lives. Rob also began to talk about the *Himeyuri Guidebook* that I have referred to several times, mentioning that if I really wanted to read a graphic account of what occurred in caves throughout Okinawa, I should read that book, and he offered to give me a copy. He told me that I would read the account of how 222 children (age 15-19) and 18 teachers from the Okinawa Female Normal School and the Okinawa First Girls' High School were drafted to work at the Okinawa Army Field Hospital in the village of Haebaru some three miles southeast of the capitol of Naha.

These topics listed in the book's table of contents describe some of the war carnage that these individuals were forced to witness including:

- "Limbs amputated without anesthetic
- Bloated corpses as large as gasoline drum cans
- Schoolmates [who] died one after another
- Maggots eating rotting flesh
- A patient with no legs crawling in the mud"[65]

At that point in Rob's tale, intense sadness stabbed my chest and a river of tears flowed heavily from my eyes. "Okay, oookay," he said, elongating the words under his breath. Then he continued, "Do you think you're ready to see the second cave?"

"Absolutely," I replied as I sniffed and wiped away tears. Something deep inside of me knew that I had to summon up the courage to continue my journey through the jungles of Okinawa with Rob. As we left that cave to see the next one, Rob told me that this sacred site was cleaned up and the monuments and carvings made because Okinawans want this place to be remembered.

As many Okinawans have told me, the Okinawan people who perished there during WWII must be remembered. More importantly, it must be recognized as a place where nothing like this should happen again as we all try to stay at peace with each other despite our differences!

Our next stop: A visit to Shimuku Gama, the "Happy Cave"

After seeing the Dead End Caves, Rob continued my Okinawan history lesson, and we visited the "The Happy Caves" (Shimuku Gama). He told

---

[65]   Shimabukuro, *Himeyuri Peace Museum* (2016), 4.

me that as it was getting late in the day, we needed to hurry to complete our cave visit while the sun was still high. After all, we did not want to encounter any of those dangerous habu snakes in the darkness. To be perfectly honest, I was leery and petrified to take this part of the journey, which was even deeper into the jungle. I kept a stiff upper lip and again assured my Indiana-Jones-like sensei Rob that I was up for the challenge. As we approached Shimuku Gama, I noticed more signs with caricature-like images of habu snakes, warning us to be ever vigilant because we were right in the heart of venomous snake country.

While feeling terrified, I put on a brave face and acted strong, but I was totally scared! We arrived at the cave grounds and after exiting Rob's car, we walked down a long and winding dirt path. We were surrounded by heavy and lush jungle vegetation on each side that included sugar cane, bamboo, massive ferns, and elephant ears.

In the numerous jungles I have visited in my world travels, I am always in awe of how large things grow there. The tropical plants that I love as houseplants often are as massive as trees in their native environments. Rob picked up a large walking stick and muttered something about taking it "just in case!" I looked around and followed his lead by also grabbing a huge branch.

While it took a whole lot more grit, muscle, and determination to get to this cave, it was well worth it. As we reached the mouth of cave, I paused to take in the beautiful landscape and the gurgling sound of a peaceful stream that meandered alongside it. Unlike Chibi Chiri Gama, that you could not enter, I was delighted to see that at Shimuku Gama, it was fine to walk inside this humongous cave. It was a tad slippery, so I watched my every step. As we walked along a winding path, Rob told me the story of the "Happy Cave."

True Story of Shimuku Gama, the "Happy Cave"

The story of Shimuku Gama bears some resemblance to that of Chibi Chiri Gama. Yet, this tale has an unexpected ending. While only 140 people had made Chibi Chiri Gama their hiding place, approximately 1,000 other villagers from Yomitan counted on this cave to save them from the rain of rockets and mortar fire that would come with the invasion. They sought refuge there from the American forces that were already capturing the nearby areas.

Prior to moving into the cave, members of the Imperial Japanese Army had also provided propaganda-laced information to the villagers about the savage Americans, barbarians bent on raping women and killing innocent children. As was the case at Chibi Chiri Gama, the Imperial Japanese Army had equipped these people with poison and hand grenades that could be used in the event they were captured. Again, it was stressed that being killed by your own hand was a far more noble deed than getting captured, tortured, and even eaten by the American troops. Getting captured was a despicable act and an insult to the honor of his majesty, the Emperor of Japan.

Inside the cave during the invasion were two men who were relatives. One was named Heiji Higa. He had worked as a laborer in the sugar cane fields on the Big Island of Hawaii. The second man, Heizo Higa, was his nephew. He had also worked in Hawaii, but as a bus driver. Both men had known some Americans through their work in Hawaii. They spoke with the villagers about their Hawaiian experience and explained that contrary to what the Japanese soldiers had told them and based upon their own exposure to Americans, they did not believe that Americans would willingly shoot unarmed people, especially not women and children.

As these 1,000 people contemplated what they would do if captured, some were conflicted about committing suicide. They had to literally make a life-or-death choice as the American forces eventually discovered them in their secret cave hideout.

Legend has it that this brave uncle and his nephew spoke with the Americans who eventually discovered the hidden villagers. These US soldiers were stationed with mighty machine guns at the mouth of the cave. They convinced the scores of cave dwellers that they would not have atrocious acts committed upon them if they surrendered. The end of this story was the opposite of what happened at Chibi Chiri Gama.

Thankfully, everyone decided to believe what the men told them about the Americans, allowing the Higas to help their fellow villagers evacuate safely from the cave. The simple deeds of these two brave relatives helped save the lives of this big group. A monument to these men was erected on the site in 1995 to celebrate the fiftieth anniversary of the end of this war in 1945.

Since this story ended in a joyous manner, the cave received the name of the "Happy Cave."

The only nuclear bombs dropped
in the history of the world

While the Battle of Okinawa ended on June 22, 1945, after that bloody fight, the war was not officially over. Following the events at Okinawa, another major milestone in the war occurred nearby on the Japanese mainland. Under the command of US President Harry S. Truman, the first nuclear bombs ever dropped in the history of the world were detonated not far from Okinawa on the mainland of Japan. At this time, the Emperor of Japan was Emperor Hirohito (posthumously referred to as Emperor Showa).

The first atomic bomb nicknamed "Little Boy," was dropped on August 6, 1945, in Hiroshima by Colonel Paul Tibbets, the pilot of the *Enola Gay*, the Boeing B-29 bomber that released it. The second atomic attack occurred when the bomb called "Fat Man" hit its target in the city of Nagasaki, just three days after on August 9, 1945. It was dropped from a plane dubbed "Bockscar" or "boxcar," a play on the pilot Bock's name. It is estimated that this atomic attack killed somewhere between 140,000 to 350,000 people (some say it was around 200,000).

While the final reason for the end of the war has come under much debate and scrutiny, one indisputable fact is that World War II officially ended with the surrender of Imperial Japan on August 15 and the formal signing of a document to end the war on September 2, 1945. At no time has the resilient "Okinawan Spirit" been tested more than during that period. The atrocities heaped upon the Okinawan people were enormous and barbaric.

This is just a brief overview of what happened during WWII in Okinawa. The war ended in 1945 and some 16 years later, in 1961, I first went to live in Okinawa with my family. Despite this dark hour in their history, the hardy Okinawans bounced back and retrieved their trophy for being the oldest and healthiest people in the world. Rob Oechsle and his wife Etsuko explained how in post-war times, Okinawans are not only stronger from having gone through the tough times of the war, but also adamantly feel that they "do not get stressed!"

So, what are their incredible strategies for coping in the world after "bad things happen to good people"?

Okinawa was not part of Japan when my family resided there. In fact, when I first lived in Okinawa during the 1960s it was under the control of the United States. As I have mentioned, remnants of the war were everywhere in Okinawa. We learned about the war in my fifth-grade elementary school classes. Through school field trips, we visited places like "Suicide Cliff" and learned about how people had chosen to jump to their death rather than be captured. And of course, we were warned to beware of the live hand grenades and landmines that still lingered in the bamboo jungle brush that we called "the boondocks."

For almost 27 years after the end of the war in 1945, Okinawa remained under the control and guidance of the United States as part of a postwar settlement. That arrangement would change dramatically in 1972 under the Okinawan Reversion Agreement between the United States and Japan. This document, under Article III of the "Treaty of San Francisco," called upon the US to relinquish to the Japanese all rights and interests of Okinawa that were acquired after WWII. Under what was dubbed the "Reversion," Okinawa was returned to Japanese sovereignty as a Prefecture (State) of Japan. The "Reversion" officially occurred under President Richard Nixon on May 15, 1972. Despite all the grief bestowed upon these peace-loving people, for generations they have managed to stay in first place and way ahead of the world as the oldest and healthiest people on earth.

Okinawan history site you must visit:
www.RememberingOwkinawa.com, curated by Donn Cuson.

How Okinawans became the oldest and healthiest people in the world!

Despite this tragic history, Okinawans are a hardy, unstoppable and resilient people. After enduring the ravages of war, they managed to start new lives in Okinawa as well as foreign places like Hawaii. So many Okinawans went to live in or created ties with Hawaii that it is sometimes called Okinawa's "Sister Country." Many were able to rebuild their tattered lives after the war.

MRS experts have validated the claim that Okinawans earn the world's gold medal for becoming the oldest and healthiest people on the planet, even after what they endured in WWII. How did they recalibrate their lives after hardship and adversity?

Meeting Etsuko Oechsle after the caves

You may remember that I had been experiencing a terrible case of writer's block when I returned to Okinawa in February and March 2018 to show the people there my manuscript and get their opinions on it as well as do a few more interviews. I was perplexed.

I had been struggling with understanding how the tragic World War II events that occurred in Okinawa had shattered the peace, serenity and even the physical shape of this heaven on earth. I could not reconcile how all of that have could happened, but, in the end, the Okinawan people came out of it stronger and, for generations, have been the healthiest and longest living people on earth.

The reason I had gone to the caves is because I had asked Rob if he might help me better understand these dynamics. After the emotional adventure of exploring the Sad and Happy Caves, I understood why my sensei, Rob, had chosen to take me there. I recognized that, in his role as my sensei, he wanted me to experience this tragic time before telling me about the "Okinawan Spirit of Resiliency."

After visiting the two caves, Rob had one more destination in mind. He took me to his home where I met his amazing wife, Etsuko. Rob and Etsuko explained how Okinawans moved forward in a positive direction post-WWII. Together, Rob and Etsuko gave me the answers to my question and more. Here is what I learned from them about the "Okinawan Spirit" that has turned them into hearty, resilient people.

How Okinawans move from tragedy to triumph and gloom to glee

After experiencing the atrocities of war to the magnitude witnessed by Okinawans, many people would have left their baggage labeled "hope" behind. That has not been the case in Okinawa. Instead, their people emerged even stronger and today exhibit an unyielding spirit to bounce back after strife and live life to the fullest.

Part of why this happened has to do with how Okinawans handle stress. You may recall from previous chapters that stress is the enemy of growing old and staying healthy. MRS experts have found that those individuals who live the longest have learned how to handle stress and put experiences of hardship behind them. This is especially true when stress is generated by things beyond one's control.

It has also been demonstrated that those who learn how to adapt to positive or negative change in their lives and the world around them also live longer. Tragedy, loss, hard and bad times are things that almost everyone experiences in life. The chance of experiencing these things also increases as one grows older. What separates the people who live longer is that they seem to possess a greater ability to cope with those stressors and not let them totally envelop their lives.

Here are the numerous pearls of wisdom that Rob and Etsuko imparted to me about the "Okinawan Spirit" that has helped Okinawans, in their words, "have no stress." I hope that you might find their approaches as amazing as I did and can incorporate some of them into your life as well.

Why Okinawans say they do not get stressed

As you have learned, during the writing of this book, I visited Okinawa to interview people living there. They confirmed what researchers spent a lot of time and money to prove. They affirmed that Okinawans generally do not let stress dominate their lives.

Another dynamic I witnessed often when I had the healthy longevity conversation with Okinawans is that they would declare, almost out of nowhere, that "Okinawans do not get stressed!" To dig deeper into this attitude, I turned to my dear Okinawan American sensei Rob Oechsle and his wife Etsuko. I asked them a series of questions including:

- How is it that Okinawans feel that they do not get stressed?
- What do they do?
- How is it that despite the atrocities that Okinawans experienced during and after World War II, they even have the strength to claim they do not get stressed?
- What are the secrets to a stress-free life?

Why Okinawans adamantly feel that they do not get stressed?

One of the biggest "aha!" moments (and there were many) that I had about the "Okinawan spirit of resilience and bouncing back after bad times" had to do with two concepts/phrases by which they live. They are from the Okinawan dialect:

- *Nan kuru nai sa (Non-kuru-nai-sah)*
- *Shikata ga nai*

The two phrases roughly translated mean:

"Nan kuru nai sa"

"Don't worry, it will ALL work out or everything will be all right; it will all work out one way or the other."

"Shikata ga nai"

"Nothing can be done about it. It cannot be helped. What can YOU do about it? Leave it alone!"

To break it down, Rob and Etsuko explained that these concepts relate to two different aspects of stress. One phrase is used when it is caused by positive events and the other when negative circumstances happen that are beyond one's control. They explained that while stress may be triggered by both positive and negative aspects of life, how each of us responds to it differs greatly. They mentioned that the phrase uttered when stress is caused by a positive occurrence is:

"Nan kuru nai sa"
"Don't worry it will ALL work out or everything will be all right; it will all work out one way or the other."

Conversely, people articulate stressful negative situations by using the words,

"Shikata ga nai"
"Nothing can be done about it. It cannot be helped. What can YOU do about it? Leave it alone!"

Here is an example that illustrates the difference between these two types of stress and the stress-resistant attitudes that people take towards them. A positive life situation such as a wedding is cause for celebration, but for some, it can produce a ton of stress.

Imagine a bride is heading to her wedding, but traffic is backed up for miles. She will get to the church a tad later than she had originally expected. Instead of fretting about being a few minutes late, the bride's mother might turn to her and say, "Nan kuru nai sa." In other words, "Don't worry, it will all work out or everything will be all right; it will all work out one way or the other."

Now imagine it is the day after the wedding and the bride and her new husband are in a car on the way to catch a plane at the airport to their honeymoon in Hawaii. Her spouse is behind the wheel when, suddenly, the car is involved in a chain-reaction car crash caused by a drunk driver. The couple's car spins out of control, hitting the car in front of them. Unfortunately, the person in that vehicle is killed in this terrible random accident. Eyewitnesses at the scene confirm that the bride's husband had absolutely no control over stopping it from happening.

The bride calls her mother, who rushes to the scene to console them. The bride and her husband still have enough time to catch their plane, but now feel guilty about leaving for their trip. The couple asks the mother for advice on whether they should still take their journey.

The bride's mother tells them they must go ahead with the trip and says to them: "Shikata ga nai." In other words, "Nothing can be done about it. It cannot be helped. What can YOU do about it? Leave it alone!" She then hugs her daughter and son-in-law and encourages them to go on their honeymoon and feel blessed that they are still alive and ready to start their lives together as husband and wife.

Researchers have found that another key element to successfully controlling stress is to practice mindfulness or living in the present. Often, people who succeed at stress management do not dwell on the failures and foibles of their past. Living life by constantly looking in the rearview mirror of their lives and criticizing themselves and others for their past mistakes and shortcomings must be avoided. As some might say, "Let bygones be bygones." What was done has been completed; what has passed cannot be changed.

Stress-resistant personalities

What Rob and Etsuko explained has also been demonstrated via research to be true--that those who learn how to adapt to positive or negative change in their lives and the world around them also live longer. MRS experts such as Dr. Margery Silver and Dr. Thomas Perls, directors of the New England Centenarian Study, cite the ability to cope with and handle adversity as a factor that contributes to longevity. They have coined a term to describe people who are able to resist stress in their lives: *stress-resistant personalities.* Many attribute the stress-resistant personality traits of Okinawans as one reason they were able to bounce back from what they experienced during WWII.

I am so thankful to Rob and Etsuko for their numerous pearls of wisdom about the "Okinawan Spirit" that have helped me understand why Okinawans feel they "have no stress." I hope that you have found their insights as amazing as I did. To help minimize stress, I encourage you to incorporate some of the approaches they shared into your life as well.

Understanding how the "Okinawan Spirit" leads to healthy aging

From my firsthand experience, I have found Okinawan people to be some of the nicest, most peace-loving and giving individuals that I had ever met. Scientists have found that there is something special about Okinawans and how they approach life and each other that contributes to their healthy longevity.

MRS experts on hardship attitudes & longevity

Etsuko and Rob are not alone in their thinking about the role that a "hardship-resilient attitude" plays in living longer. MRS experts and even the world's oldest living person (who has been authenticated) agree with their assessment. While the people who live the longest and are the healthiest go through their share of hardships, what separates them from those who do not live long healthy lives is their ability to develop skills which allow them to better cope with the downside of life.

Here are just a few more life lessons that Rob and Etsuko taught me about Okinawan longevity.

More Okinawan life lessons from Etsuko

When I visited her at her home, Etsuko talked about growing up in Okinawa and some principles learned from her parents. She spoke in glowing terms about the support they gave her growing up and relayed a very touching story about having patience through tribulation and knowing that help is always available to her from family. Her parents informed her that they were always there for her in good or bad times. She mentioned that they talked about how fishermen use the North Star to guide them. They assured Etsuko that, like the North Star, they would always be available to guide her.

Strong social connections and love

Like Etsuko and her family, the healthiest and longest-living people place a tremendous emphasis on the quality of their human relationships. They believe that people must stick together through the trials and tribulations of life and support each other.

In his book *Healthy at 100,* John Robbins corroborates what Etsuko's Okinawan parents taught her. He talks about the profound effect of relationships on healthy aging, saying:

> "There is an aspect of our lives that healthy traditional cultures have always understood to be of paramount importance to human happiness, well-being, and longevity: nothing is more important, they believe, than the quality of their human relationships. As individuals and as communities they are sustained through all kinds of hardships by the boundless commitment they must support one another, and they are complete readiness to provide mutual aid at any time."[66]

A belief system that says people are good

As you saw in my interviews with Okinawan people, many of them subscribe to the notion that inherently and deep down inside their souls, all people are basically good. Many of them spoke about the Okinawan people as being good and peace-loving individuals. Several individuals also emphasized the need they felt to work in their communities to make them better as well as to give back to others. For them, their responsibilities are not only to themselves but also to others in their communities. The authors of *The Okinawa Program* validate that notion:

> "The Okinawan philosophy affirms a faith in humanity,
> a sincere belief that deep down all people are good, and
> it emphasizes both personal *and* group responsibilities.

---

[66]   John Robbins, *Healthy at 100: How You Can -- At Any Age -- Dramatically Increase Your Life Span and Your Health Span* (New York: Ballantine Books, 2007), 217.

Okinawans believe that if someone fails, whether through bad luck or for any other reason, there is an obligation on the part of others to help. This is implicit in the Okinawan concept of "*yuimaru,*" or reciprocity, a philosophy that is rooted in old work-sharing practices where all villagers cooperated to help plant and harvest crops and were dependent on each other for survival...These kinds of personal relationships are powerful stuff. Our studies and others significant research show that they not only help to extend our lives but also seem to offer protection from illness. Fortunately, they are concepts that can also be integrated into our daily lives here in the West."[67]

After my meeting with Etsuko, Rob kindly dropped me back at my apartment. The next morning, on February 28, 2018, my brain was still trying to comprehend all the invaluable wisdom that Rob and Etsuko had imparted, when I wrote the following:

"I'm still trying to process and wrap my mind and emotions around the magnitude of what I saw and experienced yesterday. We must never forget the inhumane atrocities that were bestowed upon the Okinawan people."

As you can see, the day that I spent with Rob and Etsuko changed my life forever. It expanded my thinking about exactly what transpired during the war. By experiencing and viewing the actual places where the WWII atrocities occurred, I gained a more in-depth insight into the unbelievable courage it took for Okinawans to overcome what had happened to them. It gave me an appreciation for how even in the direst of circumstances, people can move from tragedy to triumph and gloom to glee.

Thanks, a billion, Rob and Etsuko, for imparting to me your amazing knowledge about Okinawa. I will also never forget that they helped me to finally remove my paralyzing writer's block by explaining why many Okinawan people adamantly feel that they have no stress.

---

[67] Makoto Suzuki, Bradley J. Willcox, and D. Craig Willcox. *The Okinawa Program: Learn the Secrets to Healthy Longevity* (New York: Three Rivers Press, 2001), 7-8.

Now, every day, I strive to minimize the stress in my life by using the attitudes I learned from those two powerful phases, "Nan kuru nai sa" and "Shikata ga nai."

When all is *not* at peace in paradise!

Okinawans enduring WWII is a strong reminder that even in Shangri-La, peace is not guaranteed. I adored living in Okinawa and have painted a picture of it as being a type of Garden of Eden. Yes, it was that to me, and numerous other people who lived there share my positive sentiments about the place. Having enumerated my kudos of the place, I must also report that even in paradise and the Garden of Eden, you will encounter snakes, snafus, and big Satan-like dangers. Yes, those things do exist in Shangri-La-like Okinawa.

Before ending this section on moving from tragedy to triumph and gloom to glee, I want to elaborate on some of the challenges that people are having keeping the powerful healthy aging practices alive with their heirs and other younger members of society. Okinawa is not without its challenges today. Here are but a few obstacles that the world's healthiest and longest-living people face as tradition collides with the modern world and technology.

Elders' concern for their children's longevity future

Many of the Okinawan elders, who have successfully staved off the hands of time, are feeling that the youth of today are not adhering to their traditional healthy ways. They worry that young citizens may be unable to continue procuring the title of healthiest and longest-living people in the world.

> *"Unfortunately, the youth in Okinawa are leaving behind some of the wonderful and healthy aspects of their culture and diet for SPAM and fast foods. This is starting to have a devastating effect on healthy aging and living long lives."*
> —MRAF

Many elders are disturbed when they see their grandchildren, great-grandchildren, and in some cases of their great, great-grandchildren involved in eating habits and practices that would have their ancestors turning over in their collective graves. They are aware that the errant behavior of their heirs and their tendency not to follow their traditional highly plant-based diet is already lowering the island's life expectancy, as Okinawan elders are outliving younger generations.

Post-war impact on Okinawan traditional diets

Today, Spam and Taco Rice are loved by Okinawans. What? The island's highly respected elders are afraid that subsequent generations will shorten their lifespans by consuming processed foods and partaking of too many meals at the numerous fast-food restaurants that have taken over the eating scene on the island. They are petrified of the artery-clogging food that has enticed their young next-of-kin. Young people frequently visit and gorge on food in places like McDonald's, KFC, Domino's Pizza and A&W Restaurants.

Unfortunately, the changes in eating habits of younger Okinawans have some very dire consequences. Medical and scientific researchers have seen life expectancy rates in Okinawa go down as islanders are moving from a plant-based diet to one that involves consumption of more fast food.

As we leave this chapter, what follows in Part V is information and life lessons from my own life. I will also talk about how going through them has made me stronger and more inspired to live a long and healthy life.

You should know that, until now, I have only revealed this information which follows to a small number of close family and friends. Some people who know me may be surprised by what I have written, but I hope that sharing this information will inspire them and others to take what has been learned to better their lives.

PART V:

THE HARDEST PART OF A 10,000-MILE JOURNEY IS THE LAST MILE!

Photo by: Rob Oechsle

CHAPTER 10:

First Steps & Last Miles: Reflections on the Running of the Boston Marathon

The ancient Chinese philosopher Lao-tzu once said:

> **"The journey of a thousand miles begins with the first step."**
> **-Lao-tzu**

I believe Lao-tzu means that if you have a lifelong goal you must accomplish, stop procrastinating. Instead, take the first step onto your challenging 10,000-mile journey.

This applies to any tough challenge in life, whether it is literally a journey you are taking to a faraway place like Okinawa, or you are striving to do something monumental like write a book, start a new business, or raise a family. As Lao-tzu suggests, take a leap of faith, and muster up the strength, courage, and determination to take the first step.

I would like to add another saying related to his sage advice. After you have embarked upon your journey and are almost at the finish line, remember that:

"The hardest part of a 10,000 mile journey is the last mile."
—MRAF

Here is an example of how this dynamic works. You decide to walk on a 10,000-mile journey to raise money for your favorite charity. It took time for you to finally make that commitment a reality, but you took that first step. You have worked tirelessly to reach your goal and are now at mile 9,999 with only one mile left to finish.

You have kept up an impressive pace and are feeling joyous with thoughts about how close you are to the finish line. Suddenly you experience a jolting leg cramp. One horrible thing after another starts happening to your weary body. Your mind races as you think: "I only have one mile left. How could these bad things be happening to me? Forget the negative talk, I must stay positive and not steer off my course."

With a half-mile to go, the finish line is in sight. Unfortunately, doubt invades your brain and fatigue fills your body. You are mentally and physically drained and about to give up. You just do not have enough energy left but realize you have come too far to give up.

Just when you are ready to stop, your body miraculously kicks back into positive gear. Your thoughts shift because you know that losing is not in your vocabulary and you cannot give up now!

You tell yourself that while you have gone 9,999 miles, the hardest part of your 10,000-mile journey is indeed the last mile!

Your feet are weary and tired, but you muster up the strength to continue. Before you know it, you are gliding across your finish line and throwing your hands up in a victory sign. Family and friends greet you with hugs, kisses, and well-wishes as you FINALLY achieve success by reaching your destination.

The moral of this story is that when faced with this dilemma in your life of getting through the last mile as you strive to fulfill your Ikigai, do not give up on your dreams and reason for being! The rewards of finishing that 10,000-mile journey and accomplishing your desired goal will be well worth the pain and agony endured.

I have always been intrigued and impressed by people who have the stamina and fortitude to endure the running of the mega-prestigious Boston Marathon. In 2018, I reflected on how running a marathon is a great example of what it may take to procure healthy longevity. The road to healthy aging is more of a marathon than a sprint. Here are some of my insights written after I had witnessed in person the 122nd running of the Boston Marathon in 2018.

Reflections on the 122nd running of the Boston Marathon

Today is a super-special day in Boston. It is Marathon Monday, April 16, 2018. Each year in my hometown, close to 30,000 runners from around the globe descend on "Beantown" to participate in the Boston Marathon. This is the 122nd running of this marathon of marathons, the longest, continually running (pun intended) marathon in the US. I am basking in the glory of winding down my adventure and attending this year's race. It is 8 p.m. at the end of Marathon Monday.

The marathoners ran 26.2 miles – think about it, how many people do you know (including yourself) that got up this morning and ran 26.2 miles? Really thought-provoking question, isn't it? The answer, I bet, for many of you, is that neither you nor anyone else in your universe accomplished that feat today. A few of you may have done that and I say kudos to you. I will venture to guess that most people reading this book probably did not run a marathon today.

I witnessed thousands of souls from around the globe who woke up probably before the crack of daylight to prepare and show up at the starting line of the Boston Marathon – 26.2 miles away in a place called Hopkinton, Massachusetts.

The weather today could not have been worse. It was raining buckets of ice-cold rain and was extremely windy. The frigid temperatures and rain made for a tough jaunt for marathoners. I had decided to go to the finish line this year to experience watching the runners finally reaching their goal and observe their reactions.

I maneuvered my way to the exact spot where the runners touch the finish line. I was amazed by reactions of runners as they ended their 26.2-mile journey. Some were uber-perky, waving their arms, flashing peace and victory signs. Others made high-five signs and blew air kisses into the cheering crowd.

Many lifted their heads to the sky as if to give thanks to someone in the heavens. Several runners were almost crawling their way to the end. A gesture I saw that put a smile in my heart was when a marathoner who looked ready to collapse gripped the arm of someone who helped him cross the finish line. Each person, in their own way, was a winner and accomplished their goal to start and finish the 122nd running of the Boston Marathon!

I have lived in Boston since 1971, but I left to flee the cold brutal winters and lived elsewhere from 2013-2015 to experience what life was like in a warmer, more civil climate. I learned some invaluable life lessons by taking a respite from this city. Leaving and then returning has shaped my existence on earth. I discovered that:

1. The grass may appear to be greener on the other side. Upon closer inspection, I found that Boston was in fact "greener" than I realized. By moving away from my beloved Beantown, I discovered how very blessed I was there. My hiatus, however, was just the break I needed to view the green grass of Boston through new lenses.

2. When I returned to Boston after two years away, I was certainly transformed into a person who was older and wiser and ready to proclaim as the classic song from the Standells goes, "I love that dirty water…Boston, you're my home."

My lessons learned from observing runners cross the Boston Marathon finish line are:

1. Hard work and stick-to-it-iveness (running for miles in the frigid and snow-packed Boston climate) *do* pay off if you just hang in there.
2. It is extremely important to live your dreams; not just think about them. If a dream never gets accomplished, you might want to kick that dream to the curb and try on another more realistic one.
3. Do not just think about your dreams – take Lao-tzu's advice and take that first step to make them materialize. Stop dreaming and start living your dreams.

What I learned today at the finish line of the Boston Marathon will help me to finish other races as I continue down many more "10,000-mile journeys" in life. In the pages ahead, you will learn about some personal hardships that I have only shared with a handful of family and friends until now. You will see how:

> *"I learned as much, if not more, from the*
> *downs as from the ups in my life."*

I am a firm believer that to reach your desired life destination, it is important to understand your history, or you are doomed to do two things:

1. You will not benefit from those things in your past that were good and still can be useful and beneficial to success and
2. You will repeat the bad things and failures that you have encountered.

This does not mean that you need to stay in the past and wallow in self-pity if life has not been so wonderful. As we have learned, the people who are the oldest and healthiest in the world do not live looking in the rearview mirror of their lives and longing for the past.

In the pages ahead, I will share some insights into my personal history so you might understand how I have emerged where I am today. My end in mind was to finish writing and get this book published. Here is some information I procured along my journey.

My "Job years": Moving from triumph to tragedy and gloom to glee.

In our lives and especially during the COVID-19 era, each of us has undoubtedly had moments of glee and gloom. How have people who live the longest and stay the healthiest gone from barely surviving to end up thriving in unimaginable ways in their post-hardship days? Our world today does still contain "stress-resistant personalities." Think about it, if you are a 110 year old, and have witnessed many historic days that have gone down in infamy. You survived the 1918 Spanish Flu Pandemic, World War I, the Great Depression, World War II, the first man to walk on the moon, COVID-19, and many other world events. Today, there are older people in Okinawa who lived through all those challenges and are now facing the latest global threats.

The previous chapter explained how Okinawans endured unthinkable hardships and gloom yet emerged with glee as the healthiest and longest-living people in the world. Recall what they did to remain positive in the face of despair. They maintained an attitude of gratitude and regardless of how bad life was for them, they helped others less fortunate. They lit their "little light" and "let it shine." Despite hard times, they started with Lao-tzu's one step to reach their goal. When they "hit the wall" almost at the end of their journey, they mustered up strength, telling themselves that "the hardest part of their 10,000 mile journey is the last mile."

They regained hope and delighted in conquering that final mile and crossing the finish line. All people, regardless of age, can help themselves to live a long and healthy life if they take that proverbial lemon and start a business to sell lemonade and more. They can be creative and produce lemon cake and lemon ice cream from those lemons they were blessed to receive.

I want to share something very personal about what I call my "Job years." Job was a wealthy man in the Bible who became a pauper and lost everything, including his family, to disease and famine. Eventually, when he had reached his 9,999 miles of running on bad luck, he was ready to drop out of life's race. His luck changed when he decided to hope. The light in his candle was lit again as he moved from gloom to glee. Job emerged a wiser man for he "learned as much from his downs as from his ups in life." Making sure to use the positive life lessons he acquired during his negative "Job years," he emerged triumphant through tragedy.

It has taken me years to tell the world about my personal "Job years." I realized while writing this book that perhaps someone else could benefit from the story of my journey through gloom and tragedy to my current road paved with glee and triumph. Here is my story.

My "Job years"

Today is Tuesday, June 22, 2021, and I am literally writing the last words in this book before turning it over to my editor and design team. At this moment I am feeling that in all honesty, my journey down the road to success has mostly been a good one, but the detours to reaching it have, at times, been horrendous and tragic. Many of my family, friends, and colleagues, especially in Boston, Jamaica, Cape Cod, North Carolina, and Okinawa, undoubtedly will be surprised if not stunned by what I am about to reveal.

Please be reassured that I am absolutely telling you the truth in this book about the highways that I have traversed in life. They have, at times, been plagued by tragedy that eventually morphed into triumph and gloom that became glee.

While my goal in writing this book was to expose you to my beloved Okinawan people, I also wanted to spread knowledge about MRAF's "8 Healthy Longevity Principles." I would be less than honest if I say that I am an expert at observing all the things I have spoken about in this book. Throughout this book, I have admitted openly that:

> **"I am a perfectly imperfect person who is striving to be perfectly perfect."**

I am human and, as such, cannot always be at my best and sometimes fall short of adhering to the principles in my life. I admit that I still have so much more to learn and explore in the world.

Trying to achieve my personal mission to make a positive, memorable difference and help others to do the same has not always been easy.

I am a work in progress and positive proof that after finally finding your Ikigai, the universe opens in magnificent ways! Prior to 2008, I had a thriving international management consulting business, which I had started after leaving my long-term career (17 years) as a healthcare executive in the Harvard Medical School-affiliated hospital system. I set out to live the American dream as a business owner and was successful.

But from 2008 until 2015, my idyllic life turned sour. Unfortunately, like many people who were impacted by the recession from 2008-2009, I lost almost everything and financially my life took a turn for the worse.

I established my first business at 123 Mount Auburn Street in a building owned by Harvard, directly in the prime real estate area of Harvard Square. My management consulting business, Fields Associates, Inc., was situated directly across from the Harvard Square Post Office with the famous 02138 zip code. We were across the street from the John F. Kennedy School of Government and the popular Charles Hotel.

My business grew and thrived. Eventually, I branched out from delivering international consulting services, keynote speeches and seminars to my global clients. My clientele included the likes of multinational Fortune 500 companies, Ivy League schools like Harvard College and Harvard Business School, and some of the world's most prestigious healthcare institutions (like the Harvard Medical School-affiliated teaching hospitals and others around the world).

Eventually, my services expanded, and I started writing books and coaching others on how to write theirs. I would eventually write seven books (this is my eighth book). I adored my life and work and traveled around the world on speaking engagements, book signings, and consulting assignments.

I appeared on CNN, ABC, CBS, FOX 25 TV, NBC, PBS, and in *Fortune* and *Forbes* magazine. For six years, in Atlanta, Georgia, I chaired a prominent international conference called the *Linkage Diversity & Inclusion Summit*. It was an amazing opportunity as I was able to work directly with superstars and thought leaders from around the world including:

- Coretta Scott King (Martin Luther King Jr.'s beloved wife)
- Maya Angelou (author, poet laureate and political activist)
- Sugar Ray Leonard (legendary boxer)
- Myrlie Evers (civil rights activist)
- Blair Underwood (actor)

My life was proceeding in such a splendid fashion when a series of devastating things changed and altered my world for years. Soon after the start of the new millennium in 2000, things gradually started to change in my ideal and seemingly perfect world.

In 2000, I divorced the love of my life. We had been together for some 33 years. On September 11, 2001, like many people in the world, everything in my life's orbit started to spin in both good and bad directions that I just had never experienced. On September 11, I was on a book signing tour for my first business book, *Indispensable Employees: How to Hire Them. How to Keep Them.*

On that fateful day, I was at the corporate headquarters of the Shell Oil Corporation in Houston, Texas, doing a three-hour seminar and book signing. I will always remember where I was that tragic day. On that morning, I was standing in front of a packed room of Shell Oil people attending my seminar.

About a half-hour into my program, a rather official-looking Shell Oil person entered my seminar room and said, "I am sorry to interrupt your seminar, but I need to inform you that two planes from Logan Airport in Boston have crashed into the World Trade Center in New York City. A third plane has gone down in a field somewhere in Pennsylvania and a fourth one has plowed into the Pentagon in Washington, DC. We are not cancelling anything, we just wanted you to know what is happening and will keep you posted."

The Shell Oil spokesman abruptly left the room and everyone in the room froze and remained silent. I had to quickly wrap my mind around the information that had just been transmitted – after all, I still had close to two hours and thirty minutes before my seminar would close. I vividly remember the first words out of my mouth after his exit. I gazed into the audience and said something stupid: "Do you think anyone got hurt?"

Duh? But that was all I could think to say at that crucial moment. Someone in the back of the room replied to my dumb statement by saying, "I think if those planes crashed into the World Trade Center, you can bet some people got hurt!"

At that point, I did feel terribly stupid, but a little voice in the back of my mind said, *pull yourself together, Martha. The show must go on!* The show did go on, and, like many people traveling at that time, I found myself stuck in Houston for many days before I could finally fly back to Boston.

Somehow, the events of September 11 would be a foreshadowing of some bad news for the entire country as well as for my personal life for many years. By 2008, the economy was tanking big-time. I, like many other business owners at the time, was impacted by those tragic economic times.

In 2010, I had an opportunity of a lifetime when I founded a Global Diversity & Inclusion Summit at Harvard University. Prominent people from around the world supported me and that endeavor, which was held in the fall of 2010. After that time, both my personal and professional life shifted, and I found myself, like so many others during those years, under a tremendous amount of pressure and economic uncertainty.

I call the period starting in 2008 my "Job years." Like Job in the Christian Bible, I suffered just about every type of crisis imaginable between 2008 and 2020. My life seemed to be characterized by doom and gloom as I battled the following:

- Divorce
- Foreclosure
- Bankruptcy
- Unemployment

- Homelessness
- Declining health issues
- Being flooded out of my home during COVID-19 and having to find a new one
- Almost losing my eyesight in *both* eyes during COVID-19 and having to undergo surgery to have it restored.

In 2013, things had hit rock bottom and I knew that I had to leave my beloved Boston and try to look at grass that might be greener elsewhere. I spent time from 2013 to 2015 outside of my hometown in Boston. I lived with family and friends in North Carolina and Jamaica. I could not find employment, and, at one time, was forced to take a job working at Walmart in Cary, North Carolina, to at least have some money.

My dear sister, Betty Graves, took me in during those dark days and allowed me to stay with her at her lovely home. At one time, I was feeling so down and said to her, "Betty, I never thought that my life would end up like this. *Never.* I am homeless, penniless, and must fold clothes at Walmart to have a few coins to live off. I'm just so sad!"

My sister looked me squarely in my eyes and said, "First of all, you are not homeless. You are living in my house, and you do have a home because my house is your house. So, stop feeling sorry for yourself and never, ever again say you are homeless!" All I could do as the tears streamed like a river from my sad eyes was hug my darling sister tight.

Writing about this time brings me both profound pain and joy. While many people see me as a very social person (and I am), I am also *very* private about some aspects of my life. I did not want to speak about those excruciatingly devastating times. I had to struggle with making meaning out of what had happened to me and how my life could have taken such a turn for the worse.

I thought, *I am not supposed to be at this place.* After all, while I had to always work hard, I thought I had succeeded in life. I had it all and somehow life circumstances and economic events beyond my control had turned my idyllic life upside down. As I began to rebuild my life, I gained some comfort as I began to see that I was not alone. I discovered that many people I had previously known and others who were new to my life had also experienced similar devastation.

If you are one of those people, I hope that my story will give you hope and inspire you in some way. I finally decided to write about my personal failures and challenges because I hoped that others might benefit from my tale of woe. I also hoped that if I could help even one person who was motivated by my story that it would be worth me telling it. For anyone who is or has been in a similar predicament, I hope you have gained strength by understanding that it is possible to move from tragedy to triumph and gloom to glee. While I continue to rebuild my life and career, I am happy to report that by 2015, I started to get back on my feet and made it back to my beloved hometown of Boston.

I returned to the city with such a sense of gratitude and felt very humbled, happy, and joyous that I was able to restart and recalibrate my life. During all my ups and downs, three of my lifelong friends, Juliette Mayers, her husband Darryl Mayers, and Monica Calzolari, were always there for me. They constantly pulled me up when I was down and at times gave me "tough love" messages when I was about to throw in the towel on life. They always reminded me of my strength and God's love and plan for my life even amid adversity.

Other family members, such as my brothers Michael "Binky" Mervin and Leonard "Bud" Mervin, were also so supportive of me. I will forever be grateful to my beloved brother Michael's support and encouragement to help me live my dreams. My sister Sharon "Opie" Brown and my niece, Yolanda Brown and her husband Terry and their kids also helped me along my twists and turns of life during that time. I have identified others in my Sincere Thanks section of this book. I wanted to say thanks to everyone who was there for me during those dark, dim days of my life.

With unconditional support, love, and encouragement from some devoted family and lifelong friends, along with hard work, grit, and determination on my part, I am happy to say that I survived those hard times. I am now a woman on a mission to spread the word to others about how they too can successfully cope when faced with adversity and live long and productive lives like my dear Okinawan people.

On December 26, 2016, via a generous gift from a dear person in my life, God allowed me to finally return to my beloved childhood home at Kadena Air Base in Chatan, Okinawa. I have told that person (who wants to remain anonymous) that he helped me to check off the number one item on my bucket list, return to Okinawa. I visited my beloved Okinawa throughout the holiday season and got to ring in the 2017 New Year at the popular Hilton Resort in the Mihama American Village Section of Chatan. I started writing this book at the Sunset Terrace Hotel in Chatan on December 28, 2016.

I would have the phenomenal opportunity to travel to Okinawa in February of 2018 and would once again get to visit my dear Okinawa. On that trip, I had my first book reading at Taka Nakahashi's famous Grill & Bistro Bar Garden restaurant in Chatan. I so appreciate him for hosting my first reading, so I could share my manuscript with the Okinawan people, get their feedback, and interview many of them who are included in this book. I know many of my friends, especially in Boston, Massachusetts, Cape Cod, Jamaica, and Okinawa will be totally startled by what I have just revealed about those tough "Job years." Throughout most of those years, I tried hard to hide the adversity I was going through, so I know many will be shocked when they hear my tale of woe.

I chose to reveal this information because I am in such a better place now having gone through those devastating times. On May 15, 2015, I finally returned to Boston. I came back with so much new wisdom about the ways of the world and how to be resilient after tragic times. Upon returning to Boston, I finally realized that the grass was not greener, and the sun did not shine brighter outside of Boston. When I returned, I had to literally restart both my professional and personal lives.

In 2016, my "Job years" started to finally begin to dissipate and depart. Taking Lao-tzu's advice, I took the first step of my thousand-mile book-writing journey. That quiet period was short-lived and my Job period returned just when I thought I had escaped the grips of bad times.

When the COVID-19 pandemic erupted, I thought I was out of the clear when it came to "bad things happening to this good person." I was, however, sadly mistaken. During the COVID-19 pandemic, I got deathly sick. I was not diagnosed with COVID-19 but for close to two months I could hardly get out of the bed except to eat and go to the bathroom. Just when I started feeling better, I was struck with yet another Biblical Job-like challenge. My home in the Boston area flooded. I was forced to flee from it and would spend 42 days in a hotel located in lovely Hyannis Port, Massachusetts, just minutes from the iconic Kennedy Compound where President John F. Kennedy had resided for decades.

I had to find a new place to live because of my home flooding situation. I ended up relocating to an amazing town home on the Cape and could not be happier. But, after moving in, I started to lose my eyesight. I had cataracts in both eyes and once the quarantine was lifted and it was safe to go into the hospital, I had them removed. It was a miracle because after two surgeries, I was able to see without corrective glasses for the first time in close to 52 years. The moral of the story is that today, because of the difficult times I have endured, I am more grateful than ever for every day that I wake up without a COVID-19 diagnosis. I spring out of bed ready to continue my journey to accomplish my Ikigai, which as you may recall is: "Helping People World-Wide Find Life, Work & Healthy Aging Success!"

As we all face difficult times brought about during the COVID-19 era, the question we must ask is how we can remain positive so that healthy aging might be accomplished.

The next chapter offers insights into that topic. It explores what it takes for individuals to become what I call "Perfectly Positive People" or P3s. You will learn about what individuals who are centenarians and supercentenarians aged from 100 to 110 years plus do to stay in the healthy aging game despite COVID-19 and Job-like challenges. Here is what science, medicine and research tells us about the characteristics of the Perfectly Perfect Person that helps them survive and thrive in hard or happy times.

CHAPTER 11:

Profile of a Perfectly Perfect Person (P3)

What is a Perfectly Perfect Person (P3) profile?

In this chapter, I want to identify what is a "perfect person" in the healthy aging game. You will be introduced to my **Profile of a Perfectly Perfect Person (P3)**. It identifies what a hypothetical perfect person, who lives to be a centenarian, or a supercentenarian (100 or 110 years +), would look like if such an individual existed.

Please note that the P3 model is based on proven medical and scientific facts about healthy aging from experts around the world. I invite you to not just read but also study the **Profile of a Perfectly Perfect Person (P3)**. It can help you determine what may need to be added, subtracted, or kept the same in your life if you are striving to be a healthy aging "Perfectly Perfect Person."

Watch Your Attitude About Growing Old

P3 are not waiting for their lives to end or picking out caskets for their funerals. Instead, they believe that old age is a time to celebrate. They are poised to use all their accumulated knowledge gained by living longer to better themselves and their world. They pass their knowledge on to their heirs, family members and other people, especially the children and young adults in their communities. They believe that growing old and feeling the best they have ever in life can be accomplished. They follow a mindset that says:

You are what you think when it comes to aging and longevity. If you believe that you are "over the hill" and the best years of your life are behind you, guess what? You will become a member of the over-the-hill gang, sitting around each morning reading the obituaries and wondering if yours will be next.

There are several celebrities who have been in the public eye for decades and are still going strong in their 50s, 60s, 70s and 80s. To illustrate my point, check out the ages in 2021 of these popular people:

- While 78 years old, Mick Jagger, born July 26, 1943, may not be able to "get no satisfaction," even though he has tried and tried, he is still rocking on stage.
- Mick's singing pal Anna Mae Bullock (known as Tina Turner) was born in Brownsville, Tennessee, on November 26, 1939, and at 82 years old, she still is simply the best!
- Oprah Winfrey, born on January 29, 1954, is 67 years old and still dispensing her powerful words of wisdom and helping people around the world to find success at life and work.
- Jennifer Lopez, born on July 24, 1969, is 52 years old, gave an amazing performance at the 2020 Super Bowl and was shaking her stuff at age 50 in front of billions of people world-wide.

Like the individuals named above, P3 practice a lifestyle where they "get in the groove and move." In addition, they have a positive attitude and live each day as if it were their first *and* last. They enjoy and take advantage of all the knowledge, skills, and abilities they have acquired by growing older and use age to their competitive advantage.

> "People who grow old and are healthy view becoming an elder as the time to live and enjoy vitality and inner peace. For them, it is not a time to die and plan for their funeral."
> —MRAF

Meet 101 Years Young Anna Vieira Cabral Spencer

On February 24, 2020, I had the honor of interviewing a centenarian who was a shining example of a P3. Her name is Anna Vieira Cabral Spencer. Fate has a way of putting you in touch with the right people at the best time. Such was the case with my fortuitous encounter with the 101-year-old Miss Anna. My company, OKI ME, LLC, had been conducting consulting work at Brown University in Providence, Rhode Island. Through that project, I met Miss Anna's niece, Vanessa Britto, MD, who is an esteemed medical doctor and a senior executive in the department at Brown that I was working with to create a strategic plan for the Division of Campus Life.

In a conversation I had with Dr. Britto about this book, she revealed that her Aunt Anna was a centenarian. She also showed me a fantastic video from her 101-year-old aunt's 100th birthday party. It included a lively and well-produced video where family members paid tribute via music, word, and dance to their beloved aunt, mother, grandmother, and friend.

Miss Anna has lived a vibrant and amazing 101 years. She grew up in a rural area of North Providence, Rhode Island, and believes that it was important to stay active in her community and at home. She was married and raised four sons and had dedicated her life to, as she said, "Helping and doing good." Part of her doing good was to help people from Cape Verde to immigrate to and become acclimated to life in the United States. Cape Verde is an archipelago in the Atlantic Ocean off the western coast of Africa near Senegal. Miss Anna also has been a person who has stayed extremely active as the mother of four boys, but also as a person who worked to make her community better.

I wanted to hear directly from centenarian Miss Anna about her thoughts on healthy longevity. Here was her sage advice:

> **"Enjoy life. Help people when they need help. Give them good advice. If they take it, that will be fine."**
> **-Anna Vieira Cabral Spencer**

When I asked about her proudest moment in life, she responded by saying that she "had so many proud moments." She did mention that the first time she voted it was for Franklin Delano Roosevelt and that he was a good president! Unfortunately, in December of 2020, Miss Anna died of COVID-19. May she rest in peace.

Profile of a P3
The "Okinawan Spirit": No Word for Retirement

As Miss Anna and researchers have shown, adopting a "keep on moving attitude" is one way people can increase their life spans. Many P3 may stop working in a job, but never retire from participating in and working on the causes dear to them. Interestingly, there is no word for *retirement* in the traditional Okinawan dialect. Older people who are sedentary tend to die younger, while those who "get in the groove and move" and continue learning each day live longer and healthier lives.

> **"Grow old to live and not to die."**
> -MRAF

The Eight Characteristics of a P3

Thanks to the research of MRS experts, we know exactly what type of people, if they existed, would be flawless at growing old yet staying young and healthy.

Here are Eight Characteristics of a
Perfectly Perfect Person (P3)

1. Purpose
2. Peaceful people and places
3. Principles
4. Predominately plants
5. Positive and perky personality
6. Persistent yet patient
7. Party person
8. Possibilities

What follows is a description of the eight characteristics of a P3.

Purpose

➢ **P3 have found their purpose/Ikigai (Reason for Being/Waking up).**

Because P3 have done the work, they have found their Ikigai (Reason for Being). They wake up every morning excited and ready to fulfill it. They also understand that their Ikigai is not about doing something that is selfish or self-centered but is about giving back to the world.

By finding their Ikigai, they are likely to add seven good years to their lives, according to expert Dan Buettner. To finally find their Ikigai, they have answered these four questions:

1. What do I LOVE to do?
2. What am I GOOD at doing?
3. What does the WORLD need? (The world consists of my family and friends, community where I live, my religious and/or spiritual networks, and the wider world.)
4. How can I get PAID to fulfill my Ikigai?

➢ **P3 have a belief in a higher power that seeks perfection from believers and requires that they seek a greater good over evil.**

P3 have faith in a higher power that helps to steer them in the right direction.

As mentioned, people living in the "Blue Zones" tend to belong to a faith-based religious and/or spiritual group of like-minded people. They surround themselves with others who have the same belief system. They also participate in organizations that espouse their belief system and serves as a support network for its members. By participating at least four times monthly in such groups, they can add from four to fourteen more years onto their lives.

Peaceful people and places

> ➤ **P3 are peaceful people and work to help others, including family, friends, and even strangers.**

Rather than waiting for others to do all the heavy lifting to make the communities they live in better, P3 are active participants in improving their environments. They seek peace and want to leave the world in an improved state.

> ➤ **P3 have a belief system that says people are good. They are ready and willing to help others.**

P3 subscribe to the notion that deep down inside, people are basically good. They also work in their communities to give back to others.

> ➤ **P3 are caring and believe in assisting others throughout all stages of life and in difficult times.**

P3 feel it is their responsibility to reach out to help those who are less fortunate or have fallen upon hard times regardless of what stage in life they occupy.

> ➤ **P3 believe in living in places that are peaceful. They adopt a lifestyle like that of the people who live in the Blue Zones.**

P3 understand that their lifestyle and environment are essential ingredients in the healthy aging recipe and seek environments filled with calm and tranquility.

> ➤ **P3 have a need to live in and make sure that they help to create a place in their homes and communities that are supportive of all group members.**

P3 would adhere to the proverb that "you are the people you eat and sleep with," or "Birds of a feather flock together". In other words, either live in a community or family with like-minded people or wallow with pigs in evil places. They would say that their community and surroundings should reflect the good and positive things in life.

They recognize that if they associate with people who are toxic and negative, there is a high likelihood those behaviors are contagious. Instead, they align themselves with people who can support them to do two things. First, they try to change their environment and replace negative or toxic people with those more in line with the positive things in life. If that does not work, they find or build another community. This extends to both the people in their personal lives as well as coworkers and colleagues in their jobs, volunteer groups, or community, civic and social activities.

➢ **P3 have a tradition and belief in their communities that honor the elderly and treats them with dignity and respect.**

P3 are part of societies that have a hearty respect for elders. They see elders as the bearers of knowledge who pass it down to their descendants and others in their beloved communities. In those places, the elderly are revered and honored for their feat of aging well.

In many cultures, multiple members of a P3 extended family live together. Family members want to take care of their elderly members. Older people want to play vibrant roles in the family and relish taking care of children and teaching younger people. They are serious about their roles as sensei (teachers).

Healthy Longevity Principles

P3 adhere to MRAF's "8 Healthy Longevity Principles" that are commonly practiced by people in all five Blue Zones. These include the following:

➢ **They are disciplined about their diet. They practice hara hachi bu and eat only until they are 80% full.**

P3 are not obese and do not overindulge. They eat in moderation and understand the Okinawan proverb, "Food is medicine" and eating only until they are 80% full.

➢ **P3 create ways every day to relax and unwind with "Wine @ Five" with family, friends, and colleagues.**

As part of a daily routine, P3 imbibe and unwind with family, friends, and colleagues around 5 p.m. This becomes a specific way to stop the workday and begin personal time surrounded by people with whom they are close. Enjoying the company of their supportive network serves as an effective stress management mechanism.

They will enjoy a libation such as a cocktail or other alcoholic beverage in moderation (1-2 glasses per day). Nonalcoholic beverages are also acceptable; however, for maximum impact, their libation of choice is red wine because it contains healthy aging flavonoids. The beverage with the biggest health and longevity bang would be a red Cannonau wine from Sardinia, Italy. Numerous MRS experts caution against overworking and emphasize the need to take time every day to relax, unwind, and socialize with family, friends, and colleagues. They also make sure to get a good night's sleep to rejuvenate their bodies so they can wake up rested and excited to fulfill their Ikigai every day.

➢ **P3 make sure to shake off stress and not carry it around.**

They are very much aware of the devastating effect that chronic stress has on their ability to live a long and healthy life. They take care to minimize the amount and intensity of stress in their life. They also understand that if they do not handle both good and bad stress properly, they run the risk of causing devastating damage to their health.

➢ **P3 find ways to find downtime from their work grind every day.**

P3 know that while they enjoy working and getting in the groove and moving, it is also essential to put an end to work and relax. This can include taking a siesta or power nap in the afternoon following lunch or finding time to meditate and reflect on their blessings.

➢ **P3 develop mechanisms to help them get in the groove and move by staying active and natural exercise.**

P3 know that sedentary living is their enemy. They are diligent about staying active, especially as they grow older. They participate daily in natural movement that provides exercise. This includes such things as gardening, walking, swimming, the "soft" martial arts, and dancing. In Okinawa, people like dancing to sanshin. Participating in fun social activities like karaoke is another favorite pastime a P3 might enjoy. One of my all-time favorites is taking a walk on a sandy beach (like in Okinawa!). Other beach favorites include the West Dennis Beach and Hyannis port on Cape Cod, Massachusetts and the Seven Mile Beach in Negril, Jamaica.

➤ **P3 have developed a "hardship-resilient attitude."**

P3 understand that hardship and challenges are a part of life. When tough times come into their universe, they find ways to face them and figure out how to respond and not succumb to the chaos, choosing instead to learn how to adapt to the change. They know about the power of positive thinking and have a hardship-resilient attitude. To do so, they practice mantras like "Nan kuru nai sa," meaning "Don't worry; it will all work out" and "Shikata gai nai," meaning "There's nothing you can do about it."

➤ **P3 have a need and strong desire to always put family (immediate, extended, and adopted) first.**

P3 belong to a strong and supportive family that believes in respecting and always putting family and friends first.

➤ **P3 believe in "letting their little light shine" by staying positive in both their actions and words.**

They are excited about helping others to ignite their little lights to also shine and make a positive and memorable difference in the world.

Predominately plants

➤ **P3 have a staple diet that is predominately plant based and consists of green leafy vegetables, beans/legumes, and fish.**

A huge part of their dietary intake comes from the consumption of foods that are often grown in their gardens. They spice up their lives by adding garlic, ginger, and turmeric to tasty dishes. Some do eat meat, even pork, but only in moderation. They also enjoy a good piece of dark chocolate.

Positive and perky personality

> P3 possess a positive and perky personality.

Numerous studies have identified the personality traits of people who live long and healthy lives. They reveal that they tend to not only possess positive and perky personalities but are overflowing with optimism. They are generally liked by many people, and humorous sayings and actions are a part of how they express themselves. They are often, considered to be what Okinawan's call, "taygay," which means they are "nice, pleasant, no worries, calm, relaxed, and laid-back." People enjoy spending time with them, as their lovable attitudes are contagious.

> P3 have a "go with the flow attitude." They are not bound by rigid timelines. Instead, they often "let the day take them to where they are supposed to go."

When things in their day misfire and do not go as planned, no problem, no worries. They simply resort to finding other possibilities, then continue their journey along their road to success.

P3 believe that, regardless of how bad and hard things may be in life, things will ultimately change for the better. They do not necessarily wait for the change to occur but work to make the change happen. The authors of *The Okinawa Program* offer these insights to personality and aging:

> "Personality has long been considered an important factor for healthy aging and has been studied extensively. Most studies agree that there are several key personality characteristics that are important for healthy aging: easy-going, cheerful, self-confident, adaptable, active, independent, creative, happy, high tolerance for frustration being mentioned most often. The traits that lead to an

unhealthy shorter life: Being repressed, dogmatic, hostile, neurotic, angry, guilty, sad, fearful, anxious, depressed, and aggressive."[68]

Persistent yet patient

➤ P3 are persistent in their pursuits yet patiently wait for them to materialize.

A recurring theme when I searched for information on the characteristics of people who age and stay healthy (especially centenarians and supercentenarians) is that they are decisive and persistent. They tend to know what they want and possess the patience and fortitude to work at getting to their desired outcomes. They also have the stick-to-itiveness to keep trying to achieve their goals despite the obstacles and setbacks they may encounter.

Party person

➤ P3 party to celebrate accomplishments, life's rites of passage, and milestones. They create, shape, and share positive memories with family and friends.

MRS experts underscore the importance of maintaining healthy social connections to live a long and healthy life. Whether by creating and maintaining a lifelong friendship or by participating in faith-based, religious, or spiritual ties, enjoying and keeping in touch with people is important. P3 are masters at creating and cultivating social connections. They also find ways to celebrate via parties and social events. This includes congratulating others as they accomplish goals or move through major milestones. They may organize fun times but also attend those given by others. If health concerns prevent them from socializing in person, they understand that being physically distant is no cause to be socially distant from family and friends.

[68] Makoto Suzuki, Bradley J. Willcox, and D. Craig Willcox. *The Okinawa Program: Learn the Secrets to Healthy Longevity* (New York: Three Rivers Press, 2001), 245.

Once at a party, they are most likely making people laugh through their jokes and stories. They even participate in singing a song at karaoke or dancing along with others in a popular line dance like the Electric Slide, Country Square Dance, Bunny Hop, or Cupid Shuffle. Enjoying life and helping others to do the same nurtures their social connections and serves as a mechanism for them to "get in the groove and move!"

Possibilities

> **P3 have a child-like curiosity about the world. They like to explore new possibilities with fresh, youthful eyes.**

P3 are like young children ready to discover the wisdom and riches that the world has to offer them. Instead of saying that they do not like something, they take the approach of "I'm going to try something before I say that I don't like it." This attitude keeps them young in their hearts.

> **P3 are not pessimistic but believe in the possibilities and potential for opportunity in life.**

They persist through the ups and downs and twists and turns that the world places in their path as they maneuver through time. Regardless of difficulty, hardship, or challenge, they have hope that things will turn out exactly as they should and at the appointed time that they are destined to occur. Hardship and heavy burdens are overcome by not wallowing in defeat, but by learning how to adapt, be flexible, and move on when undesired change is necessary. Because they have found their Ikigai, so each day presents an opportunity to realize possibilities, even those that may have seemed insurmountable and unobtainable.

Each day, P3 remind themselves that, as the proverb goes, "There is nothing they can do to change the past because it has come and gone. The future is uncertain and has yet to arrive. What is certain is that they must stay mindful and live in the moment. Enjoying and making the most of each second in real time is a gift, which is why it is called the present."

> **P3 are healthy most of their lives and usually die quickly.**

MRS experts tell us that when P3 finally reach death's door, they die quickly with little pain and have probably only experienced serious illness in the last one to two years of their lives. Medical experts call this phenomenon "compression of morbidity."

Happy tears fall from the saddened but enlightened eyes of those family and friends that P3s have left behind. As they pause and take the time to pay homage to a beloved P3, they also feel inspired by the powerful legacy and life lessons that many P3 have left behind. They recognize that the P3 made a positive, memorable difference in the world and helped others to do the same! What a way to go!

Now that you have learned the eight characteristics of P3, I have a few things in the next chapter that I would like to add as a postscript.

Chapter 12:

Postscript: December 28, 2016, to June 23, 2021

As I complete writing this book on June 23, 2021, after a more than five year journey, I am reminded of the quote below:

"The two things you can be certain of in life are:
1. that you were born
and
2. someday you will die!"

"It is often said that people on their deathbed don't wish that they had sent another email or gone to another business meeting. What so many people lament is that they never told special people in their lives that they loved them. Some wished they had lived life in the moment and enjoyed listening to the sound of the birds and wind."
—MRAF

Surviving and Thriving after the COVID-19 era

My journey writing this book began when I left Okinawa in 1964. It continued when I first went back to the island from December 26, 2016, to January 6, 2017. I had a 52-year hiatus from my Shangri-La on earth but understood why it was so important for me to have returned. I started to write this book on December 28, 2016, at the Sunset Terrace Hotel, not far from where I had grown up on Kadena Air Base in Chatan.

After returning to my other beloved hometown, Boston, Massachusetts, on January 13, 2018, I set a goal to finish writing the book no later than January 18, 2018. This is my eighth book, and I have never missed a book final deadline with the other seven, but that was not the case with this one.

While I made completing this book the top priority in my life, that deadline of January 18, 2018, came and went, and I still was not finished writing all I wanted to say about Okinawa and the other four places where people live the longest and are the healthiest in life. I would not finish writing my first draft of the manuscript until almost a month later.

To my delight, I was gifted one more trip to Okinawa and had the opportunity to take my manuscript directly to my beloved Okinawan people. On February 22, 2018, I set sail for my second trip to Okinawa.

On that voyage, I was elated with the interviews and insights I collected in Okinawa. Upon returning to Boston, I felt sure that I would finish writing the book in about a month. Unfortunately, my timing was off and only on June 23, 2021, more than five years after starting it, was I finally able to say The End/Sayonara to this book project.

It has been, by far, one of my most challenging but cherished book writing journeys. I am exhausted, but also exhilarated to finally complete this book. As I wind down writing, my hope is that the insights that I have provided will, in some small way, help you to wrap up your own long personal trip to health and longevity, as I am doing now. Remember that:

"THE JOURNEY OF A THOUSAND MILES BEGINS WITH THE FIRST STEP."
—Lao-tzu

And my response to Lao-tzu's saying:

"THE HARDEST PART OF A 10,000 MILE JOURNEY IS THE LAST MILE."
-MRAF

By reading my book, you have taken the first step to FINALLY finding your Ikigai Reason for Being!). Stay the course. Eventually, you will approach the 9,999th mile and have only one mile left before saying The End/Sayonara to your own journey. Life circumstances may start to erode your strength and detour you from completing it. Do not give up when you hit this "Heartbreak Hill" point on the road to success. You are almost at the finish line of your personal Boston Marathon.

Keep your stride and, as the old song lyrics go, "Walk on. Walk on with hope in your heart, and you'll never walk [or, in this case, run] alone." Think about achieving healthy aging like the people of Okinawa and the other "Blue Zones." It is within your power. As discussed, your genes will only impact your ability to live longer by around 25 to 33 percent. Your attitude, lifestyle, and environmental choices, however, will account for 67 to 75 percent of your success. Armed with a positive, hardship-resilient, and stress-resistant attitude, you can expand your possibilities for living a long, healthy, and happy life.

I have experienced unbelievable highs like getting married to the love of my life and raising a stepson and my daughter. I have also experienced the lowest of lows like watching my love and marriage sour and becoming a divorce statistic like about half of my fellow Americans. I also endured unthinkable tragedies like seeing my father die of diabetes after both legs were amputated and being alone with my mother when she took her last breath. My first business was a casualty of the recession that lasted from June 2007 to December 2009.

Little did I know that in life, I would witness the man I married and then divorced, one who had a master's degree and a doctorate from Harvard and who served as a college president, would be the target of the dreaded Alzheimer's disease. I never imagined that long after we divorced, I would be called upon to help him move out of his comfortable home and get settled into a nursing home. I have a saying that regardless of your educational pedigree, when Alzheimer's come a-knocking, the brain goes a-walking!

I have discovered that driving through life requires one to maneuver through twists and turns, detours and downturns. I hope that by reading this book, you have acquired some wisdom about what steps you can take to improve your chances at healthy longevity and emerging a winner when life gives you lemons that cannot be made into lemonade.

I am reminded that February 2, 2019, was the last Super Bowl Sunday before the COVID-19 pandemic would make football games unable to be played in person for a while. This 54-year-old event would attract billions of viewers as the world was poised for some great football between rivals, the Kansas City Chiefs, and the San Francisco 49rs. It was amazing that after 50 years of not winning a Super Bowl, the Kansas City Chiefs finally achieved what to some seemed like a miracle…they won the Super Bowl— the biggest, most prestigious football game on the planet.

Before this game, the Chiefs' coach, Andy Reid, had earned the unflattering moniker of the person who coached the most losses in the history of the game. Life, however, has a way of changing things for the positive even when long-term negative things happen to us. What a difference a game makes, as he has now been dubbed, "The coach who persevered and after 50 years of losses, won the Super Bowl!"

No matter what age you are, healthy aging can become a part of your life. On Saturday, February 22, 2020, my beloved sister Betty Graves offered this sage advice about moving from gloom to glee. She told me,

> **"Life sometimes throws you curve balls. Either you're**
> **going to die from them or grow from them."**
> **-Betty Graves**

Many authors describe the process of writing a book as like birthing a baby. I absolutely feel like my book baby has been born and is ready to enter the world. I wonder about the world my baby book will encounter. Here are my thoughts as I write the end and sayonara to this baby book.

- We never know how life may present ups and downs that must be navigated. Just before the 2020 Grammy awards, on the morning of January 26, we learned that basketball super-legend Kobe Bryant had been killed in a helicopter crash along with his daughter and seven other people. The irony is that on the same day he was killed, the Grammys were to take place that evening at the Staples Center, also known as "The House that Kobe Built."

- While none of us know exactly when our #24 jersey may be retired and we go on to that great place to be with our God, we do know that we can make the best of our lives while we are blessed to be on this earth.
- Please remember that you have more control than you think about how to achieve healthy longevity.

"Understand the incredible personal power you possess to achieve a healthy, long life. It is mostly not your genes and ancestry but your ability to create a positive lifestyle and environment that will determine your success at achieving healthy aging!"
-MRAF

By incorporating into my life what I have learned since 1961 from my beloved childhood home of Okinawa, I have weathered life's storms. Like the Okinawan people, I continue to practice what I learned from their culture as a child. I continue to work on my Ikigai, which is:

"Helping People World-Wide Find Life, Work, & Healthy Aging Success!"

Now that I have finally found my Ikigai, I have found life and work success and wake up thrilled every day to fulfill it. I wish you much luck as you take that first step toward your journey of an Ikigai-filled, joyous and prosperous life! I have another pearl of wisdom for you, and it comes from American icon Benjamin Franklin, who said:

"If You Fail to Plan, You Plan to Fail!"
-Benjamin Franklin

I urge you to heed Ben's advice and take the necessary time needed to plan what you need to do to be successful at work and in life.

Reflections on Mount Fuji and FINALLY finding life and work success

On January 9, 2017, I had the incredible opportunity to take an all-day tour from Tokyo to Mount Fuji, where I snapped this picture of that majestic and iconic Japanese mountain. Mount Fuji was a location on my bucket list. As I moved to take "visiting Mount Fuji" off my to-do list and onto my "done" list, I had to pinch myself to make sure what I was seeing was in fact real.

Photo by:
MRAF Mount Fuji, Japan

I vividly remember when I stepped off the cable car that carried my Gray Line Tour to about as high as we could go to the summit. It was cold up there and I literally froze in place as my eyes gazed upon this awe-inspiring mountain.

A funny thing happened to me at that moment. As you have read, I am a mega-music fan and a certain song flashed through my mind. It was the classic Motown hit, "Ain't No Mountain High Enough." This solid gold oldie-but-goodie was released just a few years after my family returned to the United States from Okinawa. It was sung by the late legendary R&B super-singing couple Marvin Gaye and Tammi Terrell. Looking at the snow-capped mountain, I could not help but hum the lyrics to that catchy tune:

"Ain't No Mountain High Enough to Keep
Me From Getting to You, Babe!"

After singing the song softly to myself. I started to personalize the words and began singing my altered lyrics, which were:

"Ain't No Mountain High Enough to Keep
Success From Getting to You, Babe!"

Me on Mount Fuji in Japan, January 2017

Poems about Success

I will end with two of my favorite poems, which I hope will inspire you in your healthy longevity quest. The first is often attributed to Ralph Waldo Emerson. Others argue that it is a was written by Bessie Stanley. The second is a reminder about even though we may not physically live in a "heaven-on-earth place like Okinawa, it can be inside of you if you follow some of what you have read. I hope both poems give you inspiration to Finally Find YOUR IKIGAI and achieve Life, Work, & Healthy Aging Success!

"Success"

To laugh often and much;
To win the respect of intelligent people
and the affection of children;
To earn the appreciation of honest critics
and endure the betrayal of false friends;
To appreciate beauty, to find the best in others;
To leave the world a bit better, whether by a healthy child,
a garden patch or a redeemed social condition;
To know even one life has breathed easier because you have lived.
This is to have succeeded.

Variously Attributed to Ralph Waldo Emerson,
Bessie Stanley Smith, and several others.

Photo by: Rob Oechsle

Dance
As though no one is watching you,

Love
As though you have never been hurt before,

Sing
As though no one can hear you,

Live
As though heaven is on earth.

-Father Alfred d'Souza

In closing, I wish you much good fortune on your trip to growing old and staying healthy. It is my hope that you will never forget that: *"Ain't No Mountain High Enough to Keep Success From Getting to You, Babe!"*

It is my dream that you enjoy this book and will take at least one thing or more that you can adapt to your life on your road to finally achieving life and work success. Keep in touch and let me know about your progress. I can be reached at:

martha@OKME8.com or visit *www.OKME8.com.*

Here is to you living a healthy, happy, and prosperous life filled with purpose and passion!

Chapter 13:

Gain More Knowledge

I encourage you to continue your learning by using the information below or visit my website at www.OKME8.com to:

- Expand your knowledge through additional resources such as research, books, online services and
- Increase your chances of achieving health longevity in your life and at work.

Want to learn more? This section allows you to explore more in depth what you have learned from this book. It contains additional information on healthy aging from the world's top medical experts, scientists, and researchers on healthy aging.

Below are lists of resources you can use to further your knowledge. Since there are constant updates relative to healthy aging, I highly recommend that you explore this topic beyond reading this book.

Now that you have finished reading this book, I hope you thirst for more wisdom on the topics presented. Good luck using the resources I have provided to satisfy your appetite for more knowledge as you continue down your personal life's healthy aging journey!

All the best,
Martha R. A. Fields

Recommended Reading & Resources

To acquire a more in-depth grasp of healthy aging, here are some of my top picks of both classic and trending resources to help you along your journey.

Bear, Sally, *50 Secrets of the World's Longest Living People,* Cambridge, MA: Da Capo Press, 2006.

Benedict, Ruth, "Patterns of the Good Culture," *American Anthropologist 1970, Volume 72.*

Bourdain, Anthony, *Parts Unknown: Okinawa Season 6, Episode 3, CNN.*

Buettner, Dan, *The Blue Zones: Second Edition. 9 Lessons for Living Longer From the People Who've Lived the Longest,* National Geographic Partners, LLC,/Washington, DC, 2012.

Buettner, Dan, *National Geographic, November 2005.*

Buettner, Dan, *The Blue Zones Solutions: Eating and Living Like the World's Healthiest People,* National Geographic Partners, LLC, Washington, DC, 2017.

Bull, Brett et al., *Fodor's Travel Japan* (New York: Fodor's Travel, a division of Penguin Random House, 2016)

Campbell, T. Colin and Cox, Christine, *The China Project: Revealing the Relationship Between Diet and Disease (*New Century Nutrition, 1996*), 69-110.*

Campbell, T. Colin, *The China Study. The Most Comprehensive Study of Nutrition Ever Conducted, and the Startling Implications for Diet, Weight Loss, and Long-Term Health (*Benbella Books, 2004*)*

Greger, Michael, *How not to Die,* Nutrition Facts.org (a strictly non-commercial, science-based public service provided by Dr. Michael Greger, offering free updates on the latest in nutrition research via bite-sized videos).

Marine Corps Community Service (MCCS), Commanding General MCIPAC, Brigadier General Paul J. Rock, Jr. *Okinawa Living,* Issue 241, March 2018, 53.

Ornish, Dean et al., "Can Lifestyle Changes Reverse Coronary Heart Disease? The Lifestyle Heart Trial, "*The Lancet 1990, 33698708):* http://www.ornish.com 877-888-3091 (accessed April 22, 2018)

Perls, Thomas T. and Hutter, Margery Silver, *Living to 100: Lessons in Living Your Maximum Potential at Any Age* (Basic Books, 1999)

Poulain Michael, Pes Gianni, Grasland C., Carru C., Ferucci L., Baggio G., Franceschi C., & Deiana L. (2004). "Identification of a Geographic Area Characterized by Extreme Longevity in the Sardinia Island: The AKEA Study." *Experimental Gerontology 39*(9), 1423-1429. doi:10.1016/j.exger.2004.06016. PMID 15489066.

Robbins, John, *HEALTHY at 100: HOW YOU CAN-at any age-DRAMATICALLY INCREASE YOUR LIFE SPAN and YOUR HEALTH SPAN,* Ballentine Books/ New York, 2007.

Shimabukuro, Yoshiko, *Himeyuri Peace Museum: The Guidebook*, Okinawa, Japan, October 2016.

Suzuki, Makoto et al., Centenarians in Japan, Tokyo: Nakayamashoten, Okinawan Centenarian Study, 1995.

Must-view resources about Okinawa

If you are interested in expanding your knowledge about Okinawa, below are some amazing resources about Okinawa that are top on my list.

Rob Oechsle's historical collections of pictures

Here is the link to Rob Oechsle's vast collection of pictures Okinawan history and memorabilia: https://www.flickr.com/photos/okinawa-soba/albums

Don Cuson's website: www.rememberingOkinawa.com

Explore Donn's comprehensive website of pictures and
valuable historical information about Okinawa.
Facebook page: Yeah... I Lived in Okinawa

I HIGHLY recommend that you check out this **Facebook page: Yeah... I Lived in Okinawa.** Thousands of members world-wide provide firsthand accounts of what it is like to live on the shores of Shangri-La Okinawa.

INDEX

Bibliography

Antonogeorgos, G., D. B. Panagiotakos, C. Pitsavos, C. Papageorgiou, C. Chrysohoou, G. N. Papadimitriou, and C. Stefanadis. "Understanding the Role of Depression and Anxiety on Cardiovascular Disease Risk, Using Structural Equation Modeling; The Mediating Effect of the Mediterranean Diet and Physical Activity: The ATTICA Study." *Annals of Epidemiology* 22:9 (September 2012): 630-7, doi: 10.1016/j.annepidem.2012.06.103.

Beare, Sally. *50 Secrets of the World's Longest Living People.* Cambridge, MA: Da Capo Press, 2006.

Beezhold, B. L., C. S. Johnston, and D. R. Daigle, "Vegetarian Diets Are Associated With Healthy Mood States: A Cross-Sectional Study in Seventh-Day Adventist Adults." *Nutrition Journal* 9:26 (2010). https://doi.org/10.1186/1475-2891-9-26

Benedict, Ruth, "Patterns of the Good Culture," *American Anthropologist, 72* (1970).

Beyond Meat, "Our Mission," https://www.beyondmeat.com/about/. Accessed 02-08-2020.

Bishop, Mark. *Okinawan Karate: Teachers, Styles, and Secret Techniques.* Clarendon, VT : Charles E. Tuttle, 1999.

Blue Zones, "How Not to Die: 9 Questions for Dr. Michael Greger," https://www.bluezones.com/2015/12/how-not-to-die-9-questions-for-michael-greger-md/. Accessed May 4, 2018.

Blue Zones, "True Vitality Test," https://www.bluezones.com/live-longer-better/#section-3. Accessed December 26, 2019.

Boston University Medical Center, "New England Centenarian Study," www.bumc.bu.edu/centenarian/ (Accessed April 18, 2018).

Boston University School of Medicine and Boston University School of Public Health, "The Framingham Heart Study," https://www.bu.edu/sph/research/framingham-heart-study/. Accessed May 18, 2018.

Bourdain, Anthony, *Anthony Bourdain : Parts Unknown,* "Okinawa," Season 6, Episode 4, CNN.

Budson, Andrew E., "What to Eat to Reduce Your Risk of Alzheimer's Disease." Harvard Health Blog, May 8, 2020. https://www.health.harvard.edu/blog/what-to-eat-to-reduce-your-risk-of-alzheimers-disease-2020050819774.

Buettner, Dan. "The Secrets of Living Longer." *National Geographic,* November 2005, 2-27.

Buettner, Dan, *The Blue Zones: Second Edition. 9 Lessons for Living Longer from the people who've lived the longest.* Washington, DC: National Geographic Society, 2012.

Buettner, Dan, *Blue Zones Solutions: Eating and Living Like the World's Healthiest People.* Washington, DC : National Geographic Society, 2015.

Buettner, Dan "Power 9," Blue Zones, https://www.bluezones.com/2016/11/power-9/ (Accessed April 18, 2018).

Bull, Brett, et al. *Fodor's Travel Japan.* New York: Fodor's Travel, a division of Penguin Random House, 2016.

Cabo, Rafael de, and Mark P. Mattson, "Effects of Intermittent Fasting on Aging and Disease." *New England Journal of Medicine,* 381 (December 26, 2019): 2541-2551. doi:10.1056/NEJM 1905136.

Catenacci, Jocelyn, "The Mountain of Youth: What We Can Learn from Okinawa, Japan." *Juxtaposition Global Health Magazine*, University of Toronto, April 2, 2018. https://juxtamagazine.org/2018/04/02/the-mountain-of-youth-what-we-can-learn-from-okinawa-japan/

Chopra, Deepak. *Ageless Body, Timeless Mind: The Quantum Alternative to Growing Old.* New York: Three Rivers Press, 1998.

Chopra, Deepak. *How to Know God: The Soul's Journey into the Mystery of Mysteries.* New York: Harmony Books, 2000.

Chronicle Staff, "Here is a List of Colleges' Plans for Reopening in the Fall," *The Chronicle of Higher Education*, April 23, 2020. https://www.chronicle.com/article/Here-s-a-List-of-Colleges-/248626

Corder, Roger, W. Mullen, N. Q. Khan, S. C. Marks, E.G. Wood, M. J. Carrier, and A. Crozier. "Oenology: Red Wine Procyanidins and Vascular Health." *Nature* (November 30, 2006), 566.

Cox, Christine, and T. Colin Campbell. *The China Project: Revealing the Relationship Between Diet and Disease.* New Century Nutrition, 1996.

Dalai Lama and Howard C. Cutler. *The Art of Happiness: A Handbook for Living.* New York: Riverhead Books, 1998.

Das, D. K., M. Sato, P.S. Ray, et al. 1999. "Cardioprotection of Red Wine: Role of Polyphenolic Antioxidants." *Drugs under Experimental and Clinical Research* 25(2-3) (1999): 115-20.

Dzau, Victor J., Sharon K. Inouye, Elizabeth Finkelman, John W. Rowe, and Tadataka Yamada. "Enabling Healthful Aging for All: The National Academy of Medicine Grand Challenge in Healthy Longevity." *The New England Journal of Medicine* 381 (October 31, 2019): 1699-1701. doi:10.1056/NEjMp1912298.

Fineberg, Harvey V. "Ten Weeks to Crush the Curve." New England Journal of Medicine (April 23, 2020) 382:e37. doi:10.1056/NEJMe2007263.

Fraser, Gary E. *Diet, Life Expectancy, and Chronic Disease: Studies of Seventh-day Adventists and Other Vegetarians.* Oxford University Press, 2003.

He W., D. Goodkind, P. Kowal. *An Aging World: 2015* (Report no. P95/16-1.) US Census Bureau, International Population Reports. Washington, DC: Government Publishing Office, 2016. (https://www.census.gov/content/dam/Census/library/publications/2016/demo/p95-16-1.pdf.)

Grensing, Lin, "Hiring in a COVID-19 World," Society for Human Resources Management (SHRM). April 14, 2020. https://www.shrm.org/resourcesandtools/hr-topics/talent-acquisition/pages/coronavirus-legal-hiring.aspx.Guinness World Records, "Oldest person ever (female)," https://guinnessworldrecords.com/world-records/oldest-person-(female)#:~:text=Share&text=The%20greatest%20fully%20authenticated%20age,France%20on%204%20August%20199. Accessed December 18, 2019.

Harvard Medical School, *Focus on Sleep* (Issue #2 of 5 in an email series), January 21, 2020. health.harvard.edu.

Harvard Medical School and Harvard Medical School Publishing. *HEALTHbeat.* https://www.health.harvard.edu/healthbeat/archive

Hogan, Howard, Jennifer M. Ortman, and Victoria A. Velkoff, *An Aging Nation: The Older Population in the United States. Current Population Reporting.* Washington, DC: US Census Bureau, 2014.

Journal of the American Medical Association (JAMA), www.jama.org and www. jamanetwork.com.

Kandola, Aaron; medically reviewed by Katherine Marengo. *"What to Know About Simple and Complex Carbs?" Medical News Today.* May 14, 2019.

Kopp, P., "Resveratrol, a Phytoestrogen Found in Red Wine: A Possible Explanation for the Conundrum of the French Paradox?" *European Journal of Endocrinology* 138(6) (1998): 619-20.

Kubler-Ross, Elisabeth. *On Death and Dying.* New York: Simon and Schuster, 1997.

Marine Corps Community Service, "Eat the Rainbow!" *Okinawa Living,* Issue 241, March 2018, 53.

McEntarfer, Erika, *Older People Working Longer, Earning More,* US Census Bureau, April 24, 2018. https://www.census.gov/library/stories/2018/04/aging-workforce.html

National Academy of Medicine, Global Roadmap for Health Longevity. https://nam. edu/initiatives/grand-challenge-healthy-longevity/global-roadmap-for-healthy-longevity/.

National Institute on Aging, US National Institutes of Health, www.nia.nih.gov.

Nestle, Marion, "Plant-Based Meat: The Cosmetic Color Problem." EcoWatch, May 23, 2018. https://www.ecowatch.com/plant-based-meat-color-2571398573.html.

New England Journal of Medicine, www.nejm.org.

New York Times Front Page, VOL. CLXIX, No.58,612, The New York Times Company, Sunday, February 23, 2020. https://www.nytimes.com/issue/todayspaper/2020/02/23/todays-new-york-times.

Ornish, Dean, et al., "Can Lifestyle Changes Reverse Coronary Heart Disease? The Lifestyle Heart Trial." *The Lancet,* 336(8708) (1990): 129-33.

Ornish, Dean, *Love and Survival: The Scientific Basis for the Healing Power Of Intimacy.* New York: Harper Collins, 1998.

Orlich, M.J., P. N. Singh, J. Sabate, K. Jaceldo-Siegl, J. Fan, S. Knutsen, W. L. Beeson, and G. E. Fraser. "Vegetarian Dietary Patterns and Mortality in Adventist Health Study 2." *JAMA Internal Medicine* (July 8, 2013), 1230-38.

Panagiotakos, D. B., C. Chrysohoou, G. Siasos, K. Zisimos, J. Skoumas, C. Pitsavos, and C. Stefanadis. "Sociodemographic and Lifestyle Statistics of Oldest Old People (>80 Years) Living in Ikaria Island: The Ikaria Study." *Cardiology Research and Practice* (2011), article ID 679187.

Paxson, Christina, "College Campuses Must Reopen in the Fall. Here's How We Do It." *New York Times,* April 26, 2020.

Pelletier, Kenneth R., *The Best Alternative Medicine.* New York: Simon & Shuster, 2000.

Perls, Thomas J., and Erwin J. Tan. "Healthy Longevity: An Introduction to the Series," *The Journals of Gerontolgy, Series A, Issue Supplement 1 Volume 74 (*November 13, 2019): S1-3. doi.org/10.1093/gerona/glz237.

Perls, Thomas, Iliana V. Kohler, Stacy Andersen, Emily Schoenhofen, et al. "Survival of Parents and Siblings of Supercentenarians." *The Journals of Gerontology: Series A: Biological Sciences and Medical Sciences.* (2007), 1028-35.

Perls, Thomas, and M.H. Silver. *Living to 100.* New York: Basic Books, 1999.

Pes, G. M., F. Tolu, M. Poulain, A. Errigo, S. Masala, A. Pietrobelli, N.C. Battistini, and M. Maioli. "Lifestyle and Nutrition Related to Male Longevity in Sardinia: An

Ecological Study." *Nutrition, Metabolism and Cardiovascular Diseases* (March 2013), 213-19.

Poulain Michael, Gianni Pes, C. Grasland, C. Carru, L. Ferucci, G. Baggio, C. Franceschi, and L. Deiana. "Identification of a Geographic Area Characterized by Extreme Longevity in the Sardinia Island: The AKEA Study." *Experimental Gerontology* 39 (9) (2004): 1423-1429. doi.org/10.1016/j.exger.2004.06.016.

Roberts, Andrew W., Stella U. Ogunwoke, Laura Blakeslee, and Megan A. Rabe. *The Population 65 and Older in the United States: 2016.* American Community Survey Reports (ACS-38), United States Census Bureau. October 2018. https://www.census.gov/content/dam/Census/library/publications/2018/acs/ACS-38.pdf.Robbins, John. *Healthy at 100: How You Can--At Any Age--Dramatically Increase Your Life Span and Your Health Span.* New York: Ballantine Books, 2007.

Robson, David, "A High-carb Diet May Explain Why Okinawans Live So Long." BBC Future, January 17, 2019. https://www.bbc.com/future/article/20190116-a-high-carb-diet-may-explain-why-okinawans-live-so-long.

Senda, Masakazu, "World's oldest person confirmed as 116-year-old Kane Tanaka from Japan." https://www.guinessworldrecords.com/news/2019/3/worlds-oldest-person-confirmed-as-116-year-old-kane-tanaka-from-japan/. Accessed December 27, 2019.

Shimabukuro, Yoshiko, *Himeyuri Peace Museum: The Guidebook*, Okinawa, Japan: October 2016.

Society for Human Resources Management, *Resource Spotlight Coronavirus and COVID-19,* April 14, 2020. www.shrm.com.

Sun, Lena H., "CDC Director Warns Second Wave of Coronavirus is Likely to Be Even More Devastating," *Washington Post*, April 21, 2020.

Suzuki, Makoto, Bradley J. Willcox, and D. Craig Willcox. *The Okinawa Program: Learn the Secrets to Healthy Longevity.* New York: Three Rivers Press, 2001.

Suzuki, M., and C. Willcox. "The Historical Context of Okinawan Longevity: Influence of the United States and Mainland Japan." *Okinawan Journal of American Studies* (2007), 46-61.

Suzuki, Makoto, Bradley J. Willcox, and Craig D. Willcox. "Implications from and for Food Cultures for Cardiovascular Disease: Longevity." *Asia Pacific Journal of Clinical Nutrition* (June 2001), 165-71.

Suzuki, Makoto, Bradley J. Willcox, and D. Craig Willcox, *The Okinawa Diet Plan: Get Leaner, Live Longer and Never Feel Hungry.* New York: Three Rivers Press, 2005.

Tappe, Anneken, "30 Million Americans Have Filed Initial Unemployment Claims Since mid-March." CNN Business, April 30, 2020. www.cnn.com.

Unilever Foods Solutions, "The Future of Meat: The Rise in Plant Based Alternatives." https://www.unileverfoodsolutions.ca/en/chef-inspiration/plant-based-eating/trends/meat-alternatives.html. Accessed February 8, 2020.

United States Census Bureau: Stats for Stories, "National Senior Citizens Day," August 21, 2019. https://www.census.gov/newsroom/stories/2019/senior-citizens.html.

United States Census Bureau, US, and World Population Clock, https://www.census.gov/popclock/. Accessed April 17, 2020.

United States Social Security Administration. Benefits Planner/Life Expectancy Calculator. https://www.ssa.gov/OACT/population/longevity.html. Accessed December 26, 2019.

Wade, Nicholas. "Gene Links Longevity and Diet, Scientists Say." *New York Times*, May 3, 2007, A20. https://www.nytimes.com/2007/05/03/health/03gene.html.

Walford, Roy. *Beyond the 120-Year Diet: How to Double Your Vital Years*. New York: Four Walls Eight Windows, 2000.

Washington Post.com. "French Scientists Stand By World's Oldest Person Jeanne Calment." January 5, 2019. https://www.washingtonpost.com/video/world/french-scientists-stand-by-worlds-oldest-person-jeanne-calment/2019/01/05/c9e46c7a-4964-4869-ae5d-4c305ff5d2bc_video.html

Weil, Andrew. *Healthy Aging: A Lifelong Guide to Your Physical and Spiritual Well-Being*. New York: Alfred A. Knopf, 2005.

Weil, Andrew. *Spontaneous Healing: How to Discover and Enhance Your Body's Natural Ability to Maintain and Heal Itself*. New York: Alfred A. Knopf, 1995.

Weil, Andrew. "You (and Your Brain) Are What You Eat." *Time*. (January 16, 2006).

Wikipedia contributors, "Amphibious warfare," *Wikipedia, The Free Encyclopedia*, https://en.wikipedia.org/w/index.php?title=Amphibious_warfare&oldid=854265489 (accessed October 10, 2018).

Willcox, B. J., D. C. Willcox, H. Todoriki, A. Fujiyoshi, K. Yano, Q. He, J. D. Curb, and M. Suzuki. "Caloric Restriction, the Traditional Okinawan Diet, and Healthy Aging: The Diet of the World's Longest-Lived People and Its Potential Impact on Morbidity and Life Span." *Annals of the New York Academy of Sciences* (October 2007), 434-55.

Willcox, Bradley, Craig Willcox, and Makoto Suzuki. *The Okinawa Way*. London: Penguin Books, 2001.

Willcox, D. C., B. J. Willcox, H. Todoriki, and M. Suzuki, "The Okinawan Diet: Health Implications of a Low-Calorie, Nutrient-Dense, Antioxidant-Rich Dietary Pattern Low in Glycemic Load." *Journal of the American College of Nutrition* (August 2009), 500S-516S.

Willcox, D.C., B. J. Willcox, S. Shimajiri, S. Kurechi, and M. Suzuki. "Aging Gracefully: A Retrospective Analysis of Functional Status in Okinawan Centenarians." *American Journal of Geriatric Psychiatry* (March 2007), 252-56.

Willcox, D. Craig, Bradley J. Willcox, Wen-Chi Hsueh, and Makoto Suzuki. "Genetic Determinants of Exceptional Human Longevity: Insights from the Okinawa Centenarian Study." *Age* (December 2006), 313-332.

Willcox, D. Craig, Bradley J. Willcox, S. Shimajiri, S. Kurechi, and M. Suzuki. "Aging Gracefully: A Retrospective Analysis of Functional Status in Okinawan Centenarians." *American Journal of Geriatric Psychiatry* (March 2007), 252-6.

Woolf, Steven H., Heidi Schoomaker, "Life Expectancy and Mortality Rates in the United States, 1959-2017" *JAMA (Journal of the American Medical Association)* 322(20) (November 26, 2019): 1996-2016. doi:10.1001/jama.2019.16932.

World Health Organization, *World Health Statistics Overview 2019: Monitoring Health for the SDGs (Sustainable Development Goals)*, (Geneva, Switzerland: World Health Organization, 2019), https://apps.who.int/iris/bitstream/handle/10665/324835/9789241565707-eng.pdf, 10-12.

ACKNOWLEDGEMENTS

A BILLION THANKS TO MY WORLDWIDE VILLAGE

It took a world village to bring this book to fruition over close to a five-year period. I want to acknowledge all the members of my global village network who helped make this book a reality.

It was a joy to work with my editor, Kate Victory Hannisian of Blue Pencil Consulting (www.bluepencilconsulting.com) and Monica Calzolari. I could have crossed my lengthy Book Marathon finish line and declare victory signs to the heavens without their help, encouragement, and unbelievable editing skills. The incredible front and back book covers were originally designed by Cindy Murphy, of Bluemoon Graphics. The front book cover portrait was shot by renowned Boston-based photographer extraordinaire Jack Rummel. Dan Searl, you have been a fabulous videographer.

Henjie Jensen did a superb job shepherding me through the Lulu Publishing process. You are an amazing professional and incredible at your job! Others assisted in the editorial process along the way, and I am appreciative of the roles they played: Ken Lizotte and Elena Petricone (Emerson Consulting), Sam Sanderson, and Dana Scott.

Kudos to my world-renowned medical team of experts, including my 25+-year association with one of the most amazing physicians in the universe, Carol Bates, MD. She is an esteemed preceptor, professor, administrator and beloved mentor at Harvard Medical School and Boston's Beth Israel Deaconess Medical Center. Dr. Jill Smith and Terri of Newton Wellesley Hospital, you do amazing work helping people to restore their vision. Dr. Chris Getchell and Dr. John DeGuzman of Tufts New England Dental School, you both are incredible.

To my colleague, Ebi D. Okara, Ed. D, Licensed Psychologist, of Metis Psychological Associates, LLC. (https//www.metis psych.com), you are a shining example of a mental health miracle worker par excellence. Your phenomenal medical and mental health expertise coupled with your positive messages and endless quotes about hope, faith and overcoming adversity are a welcome message for so many COVID-19 weary souls. You are a beacon of light for those seeking paths to maintain physical and mental health and well-being in the ever-changing landscape of the COVID-19 new world order.

Priscilla Nawachukwu, NP, also of Metis Psychological Associates, LLC., I so appreciate your unending dedication to your patients seeking to achieve peace in a world that is often chaotic and challenging.

Since 1980, when I started my career in healthcare management at Children's Hospital-Boston, I have been so blessed to be surrounded by the camaraderie of so many current and long-term Harvard Medical School-affiliated teaching hospital colleagues.

Whether as a Vice-President at a Harvard teaching hospital for close to 7.5 years or as a consultant at institutions like those affiliated with many Harvard Medical School-affiliated hospitals such as **Mass General Brigham** (the former **Partners HealthCare**), I have served for close to 40 years employed as a healthcare executive or independent international management consultant to so many world-class institutions. I feel honored to have served alongside so many stellar healthcare professions for decades. It is wonderful for so many in the public to finally recognize your tireless dedication to providing quality teaching, research, patient care, and community outreach.

I also think about how wonderful it is to see the public finally recognizing *and* acknowledging the work of those God-inspired medical miracle workers.

A special thanks to all my esteemed former and current colleagues at the Massachusetts Eye and Ear Infirmary (MEEI) where I served as a Vice President, and the Harvard Community Health Plan Hospital (HCHPH) where I was a Director. This includes the following lifelong colleagues: Arthur Berarducci, former Chief Operating Officer; Carol Covell, Joe Castellana, Amy Hudspeth Cabell, Esq., Dianne Austin, Barbara Katz, Esq., Diana Keller Fernandez; Yvonne Goulart; Jackie Rosenthal; Frank Silvia, my dear friend and skydiving enthusiast; and Carola Wilder Endicott. Sue Glover, Grace Regan, and Michael Holey at BC High, as well as Kerri Hoffman, Edwin Ochoa, and Cory Zanin of PRX, I am glad we have worked together.

I would be remiss if I did not mention my many colleagues at the Massachusetts General Hospital (aka Man's Greatest Hospital), and Brigham and Women's Hospital, including my former employee and now uber-accomplished Paula Squires, Senior VP, HR BWH, and Brigham and Women's Physicians Organization President Bill Johnston and Brooke Zeliff. Thanks to Chief Medical Staff Officer, Sunil "Sunny" Eappen, and former Chief Medical Officer, the ultra-talented Jessica Dudley, MD. Jean Jackson and Lianne Crossette of the HR Department, thanks for your camaraderie.

There are SO many to thank at Mass General Brigham (Former Partners HealthCare) including Rose Sheehan, CHRO, and Colleen Moran. Thanks colleagues Sharon Whittaker and Marcia Kimm-Jackson for your friendship.

Like the people who live the longest and are the healthiest in the world, family and friends are always placed first in my life. I am extremely blessed to have some family members who always provide me with unconditional LOVE: Bud and Samaria Mervin, and Michael "Binky" Mervin (Bink, without your unbelievable support, I would never have checked off the #1 item on my bucket list and returned to our beloved home at Kadena Air Base, Chatan, Okinawa, Japan. You are simply the best.)

Michael, Bianca, Richard and Shawna Fields and Amare and Zion, I love you all to the moon and back. Betty Graves, I will never forget your unending support, encouragement and telling me that I would never be homeless and always had a home with you when I needed one. Kiki Mervin and the Browns: Darrell, Tedra, Burrell, Crystal, Opie and Olivia, Yolanda, Terry, Landon, Holland, and Sterling Turner, you all mean the world to me.

My adopted family and lifelong friends who have been with me through life's twists, turns and ups and downs. Thank you, Mayers Family, I will always remember your love and encouragement: Juliette, Darryl, D'Anna, Danielle and Miss Ellie Mayers. Monica Calzolari, I appreciate your friendship, help on this project, and the powerful positive messages you always convey to lift me and others up.

Maria Levin and Dave Carpenter of Maria Levin, LLC, I will be forever indebted to you for believing in me even when I did not totally believe in myself. You are the "Salt of the Earth", and I would not be where I am today without your financial acumen and genius!

My Lifelong Colleagues and Friends: Johanna Cornwell, Manny Correia, Tom Harvey, General Dave Ohle, Susan Callender, Sara Glasser-Havens, Tom Bretto, Julius and Sandra Britto, Galen Henderson, Steven Norman, Jean Mojo, Mario Gapuz, Jr., Kelley Chunn, Angela Haye, Kim Cromwell, Michelle Fantt Harris,…to work with you all. Ed Hurley-Wales, Ina Lavin, Doreen Nichols, Nancy Stager, Dr. Larry Stybel and Mary Anne Peabody of Stybel Peabody Associates, who would have known since the mid-1980s and 1990s of the lasting impact that the Boston Human Resources would have on our lives for close to 35 years? Larry Stybel, thanks for serving as a mentor and as "The "Networking King of Boston," always trying to bring people together. Jackie Benson Jones of Harvard and Susan Titus Garnier and Barbara Addison Reid, PhD of Lesley University, it has been an honor and pleasure to call both of you brilliant women colleagues and friends. My colleagues at Harvard College, Harvard Business School and Harvard University, I am thankful for the opportunity to work with you all.

Brown University, I adored our strategic planning work together. Many thanks to all my colleagues in Campus Life: Vanessa Britto, MD, Eric Estes, PhD, Hieu Tran and Loc Truong, PhD. Loc, you are an incredible world-force of wisdom and positive power.

I will never forget US Airman Brianna Cotton for serving as a fabulous escort when I revisited my childhood home at Kadena Air Base Okinawa for the first time after 52 years.

I am grateful to those who live or lived in Okinawa and were interviewed and/or contributed quotes: Ms. Phai Brackett and her team at Phai's House of Jade, Okinawa; Kumiko Mituhisa, Takuya Nakahashi, Noriko Takiguchi and Emi Toma. Rob and Etsuko Oechsle, I am grateful for your warm and generous spirit and teaching me so much about Okinawa. Vicki C. Wilson and sons Jacob and Jackson, I will always remember that you introduced me to sanshin at the Bank of the Ryukyu, Naha. Wilson Family, you taught me *so* many marvelous things about Okinawa, including how to eat beni imo (Japanese purple sweet potato), Blue Seal ice cream and taco rice. Thanks, Vicki for helping me create my book title.

To my 54,000+member global cyber-family in the YEAH…I lived in Okinawa Facebook group, I cherish your individual and collective friendships and willingness to be my *senseis* and willingly share your wisdom and insights about our beloved Okinawa!

To my Friday Night Karaoke Family and Friends at JJ Grimsby's in Stoneham, MA: Joe Taliaferro, you are my kind and dear lifelong friend and Karaoke DJ extraordinaire. Thanks *so* much for being there for me when I needed it most! Dana Cox and wife, Charlotte (love your Karaoke DJ expertise, Dana), thanks for always making Minnie Riperton's "Lovin' You" sound spectacular when I sing my favorite "Go-to Karaoke tune." Bob, Cheryl, Courtney, Jamie, Joanne, Josephine, Linda, Ralph, and Sally, it is always great to get together with all of you and laugh, celebrate birthdays, life milestones, and sing along to those groovy oldies but goodies on Friday Night Karaoke at JJ Grimbsy's.

Rebecca, and her Melrose, MA team at Beacon Hill Wine, including Ashland, Eugenia, and Tara, you all are such incredibly kind and knowledgeable people. Rebecca, I love your wine education lessons about Sardinian Cannonau red wine, the best in the world for healthy aging.

I reach out with much gratitude to several people who helped me with the research and administrative tasks for this book: Marcia Manong, Sara Sezun, and Yolanda Turner. It is always wonderful to work with family members like you, Yolanda. Caritas Communities and all my friends in Melrose, I will be forever indebted for you taking me under your nurturing wing and providing me with a safe, secure, and friendly place to make a fresh start on life in Boston.

My Staples Business Team at their original HQ in Brighton, MA: Samantha "Sam," you are always *so* customer-friendly and helpful. Thanks as well to the Hyannis, MA store especially Haley, Kevin, Luke, Macaulay, Michael, and Nathan. Luke Herrling, the charts you created were spectacular as was your customer service. Thanks also to the Assembly Row Staples Copy Center in Somerville, MA: Phil, Andrew, and your dynamic team.

Stylist at Zina's Beauty Salon, my main stylist, Meka, I cannot thank you enough for always trying to transform me "from a Disaster to a Diva" when I walk through your purple doors. Thanks to Zina Thompson and Brittney Crawford for making every trip to your salon a memorable and enjoyable one.

So many people welcomed me to Cape Cod during the Summer of 2020 after I had not lived there for 20 years. This includes my hotelier friends David and Sandy Patel and Angie Brown from the Sea Coast Inn in Hyannis Port. Fred Wilson and Ms. Valrie Jarrett, I feel so blessed to have you as friends and appreciate all you did to help me move to the Cape. Kelli Orava, Mark Peterson, and your team (Mike, Lalo, Ed, Bob, and Adam) at Davenport Realty, you are all fantastic as are my friends Valary and Mark Damon, Andy

Havens, Stacey Olson, Lynn and Ron Jacoby, Valerie and Alain Fortin, Chris Terranova, and Debbie and Shirley Meymaris. Thanks Toyota Hyannis, especially Kenny, Dan, Theo, and Colleen. Officers Vello and Rosenbaum from the Newton, MA Police Department, you are a stellar example of law enforcement officials who practice positive community involvement.

To those world-renowned healthy aging experts who have paved the way for so many with their quest to advance the global Medical, Research and Scientific (MRS) knowledge and medical practices on healthy longevity/aging, I thank you for caring to share your incredible wisdom and relentless pursuit to help people worldwide become healthy, wealthy, productive and wise. My most admired favorites are: Dan Buettner, Tom Perls, MD; and Margery Hutter Silver, EdD; John Robbins, MD; Makoto Suzuki, MD; and Bradley J. Willcox, MD and D. Craig Willcox, PhD.

Thanks, a billion to all of you for helping me *finally* cross the finish line of my 10,000-mile Boston Marathon-like Book Journey!

Martha R. A. Fields
06-23-2021 (Wednesday) 8:08 am

ABOUT THE AUTHOR

MARTHA R. A. FIELDS
President & CEO
International Author, Businesswoman, Consultant, Healthy Aging Expert, Educator, and Inspirational Speaker

Martha R. A. Fields is a highly respected and accomplished international management and leadership development, diversity and inclusion, education, healthcare, and human resources consultant and business owner. A prolific writer, she is the author of eight books. They include one co-written with Ken Blanchard and the late Stephen Covey, known for the international bestseller, *The Seven Habits of Highly Effective People.* Martha also wrote a book and served as a mentor with Harvard Business School Publishing. Her eighth and latest book is: *The Okinawa in Me: FINALLY Finding My IKIGAI (Reason for Being!)* At age 33, Martha became a Vice President at a Harvard Medical School teaching hospital where she served for over seven years. She then founded and was President and CEO of two international management consulting firms. Her first company, **Fields Associates, Inc.,** was located for thirteen years in a building at Harvard University in Cambridge, Massachusetts. Her current business, **OKI ME, LLC,** is at 75 State Street, Boston, Massachusetts, next to historic Boston Harbor. Ninety-eight percent of Martha's clients report receiving outstanding customer service from her firm. She has worked around the globe with top presidents, executives and leaders from major Fortune 500 companies, prominent nongovernmental organizations (NGOs,) leading Ivy League schools, and world-renowned educational, healthcare, financial services, and retail institutions. Martha is internationally recognized as a strategic planner, connector, and thought leader. She has appeared as an expert on **CNN, ABC, PBS, FOX 25 TV, CBS, NBC** and in *Fortune* and *Forbes.* As a professional keynote and inspirational speaker, she has been eligible to receive bookings through the prestigious **Washington Speakers Bureau** and the **American Program Bureau.**

She has lived in multiple locations in the US, and in Okinawa, Japan, and Jamaica, West Indies. Her global travel has included visits to remote sites in Argentina, Brazil, and Guatemala; Machu Picchu and Cusco, Peru; the Amazon Jungle; the Andes Mountains; islands in the Caribbean; Capri, Italy and timeless European cities like London, Paris, Rome, and Madrid. Martha fondly refers to herself as a "Citizen of the USA & the World" and a "Corporate Cupid" who adores strategic planning, linking organizations and people for networking, mentoring, and work/life success so that everyone can make a positive, memorable difference in the world and help others to do the same!

OTHER BOOKS BY MARTHA R.A. FIELDS

Roadmap to Success
Co-authored with Dr. Stephen R. Covey and Ken Blanchard

This exceptional compilation of highly accomplished people reveals the roads they travelled to become successful. The book shares how they navigated their way through life's tragedies and triumphs. It also unveils their secrets and remarkable insights on how to set and accomplish goals in life *and* at work.

Love Your Work by Loving Your Life (LwL²)

Whether you are a millennial or member of AARP, this book has a message for you. Despite turbulent times and world conflict, there *is* hope. Over 150 successful leaders, Fortune 500 companies, NGOs, and average people from around the world contributed to this powerful book. Learn from their expert-tested solutions that will help you to better **Love Your Work by Loving Your Life!**

Indispensable Employees: How to Hire Them. How to Keep Them.

Despite economic highs and lows, the race to recruit and retain top talent has become fiercer and more competitive. Discover the secrets of what you as a manager or employer can do *now* to excel in todays and tomorrow's workforce game to get and keep exceptional talent. Explore best practices utilized in the past by top organizations such as Harvard University, Cisco Systems, and the US Army.

Managing Diversity: Expert Solutions to Everyday Challenges

Martha served as the mentor and a co-author of this book by Harvard Business School Publishing. This tiny pocket-sized book is packed with enormously handy tools, self-tests, and real-life examples to help you identify your organization's diversity, inclusion, and globalization strengths and weaknesses.